MERCURY READER

a custom publication

CANADIAN MERCURY WRITER

Issues in Health Science
Helen Bajorek-MacDonald

PEARSON

Please visit our website at *www.pearsonlearningsolutions.com.*

Attention bookstores: For permission to return any unsold stock, contact us at *pe-uscustomreturns@pearson.com.*

Pearson Learning Solutions, 501 Boylston Street, Suite 900, Boston, MA 02116
A Pearson Education Company
www.pearsoned.com

PEARSON

ISBN 10: 1-256-60204-3
ISBN 13: 978-1-256-60204-0

General Editors

Janice Neuleib
Illinois State University

Kathleen Shine Cain
Merrimack College

Stephen Ruffus
Salt Lake Community College

Table of Contents

Environmental Ethics

((• Listen to the **Chapter Audio** on **mythinkinglab.com**

We live in a world of limits. Population increase, unprecedented consumption, toxic waste, pollution, depletion of resources and species, and climate change have brought humanity face to face with the limits of the natural world and the environment. This realization makes it imperative that we rethink our core values and the way(s) we live. In addition, we must also rethink our relationships to the environment and obligations to one another, including our posterity. This chapter helps us think through these important issues from both Western and non-Western perspectives.

OBJECTIVES

After you have read this chapter, you should be able to

1. Recognize environmental ethical issues.
2. Understand what lies behind our attitudes toward the natural environment and everything in it (plants, trees, and animals).
3. Discern whether we have a moral obligation to preserve and protect nature.
4. Understand and deal with the question "To what extent do animals and plants have rights?"
5. Know and understand the arguments for and against the use and exploitation of the natural environment and everything in it.
6. Recognize the importance of non-Western ethical perspectives for addressing environmental issues.

DEFINITION OF KEY TERMS

1. ***Speciesism:*** A prejudice for one's own species and against other species.
2. ***Sentientism:*** The theory that only those beings with mental states should be the subject of moral concern.
3. ***Wholism:*** A conception of nature wherein humans and nature together form a moral community.
4. ***Vegetarianism:*** The refusal to eat meat, fish, fowl, or any food derived from them and the favoring of a diet of vegetables.
5. ***Endangered species:*** A species of animals in danger of becoming extinct because of the encroachment of civilization upon the natural environment and careless exploitation by human beings.

From Chapter 16 of *Ethics: Theory and Practice*, Eleventh Edition. Jacques P. Thiroux, Keith W. Krasemann.

NATURE AND MORALITY

In recent years, people have come to realize that natural resources and animals, plants, and trees are not boundless but are subject to diminishment, destruction, and loss through careless exploitation, pollution, and the general encroachment of civilization. In the past, despite inklings of this realization in cases such as the near extinction of the American buffalo in the old West through wholesale slaughter, people assumed that natural resources would last forever and were there merely to be used and exploited. Water, air, forests, animals, plants, and minerals were considered to exist in abundance and without end. In recent years, however, with the rise of industrialized, technological, producing, and consuming societies, people have discovered that this is just not so. There indeed are limits to the natural resources of the world, and it is possible to eliminate whole species of animals by means of lack of concern for their survival and willful exploitation.

At this point one may wish to review the discussion of the four aspects of morality, and especially the second aspect, nature and morality, which has to do with human beings and their relationship to nature. For most modern, "civilized" people, "nature and morality" was a new category, but in reality it was an ancient idea among primitive human beings who tended to see themselves as being much more closely allied with nature than we do. Even our modern-day concerns are often centered around nature's destruction as that affects our own lives rather than nature having value in and for itself. In this sense, human relations with nature could be subsumed under the social aspect having to do with people in relationship to other people.

However, many people do consider nature as being valuable in and of itself and insist that we have specific moral obligations toward it and all that it contains, especially those animals that are close to us in nature's order. In this chapter, we will look at both aspects but will concentrate upon nature and morality.

ENVIRONMENTAL ETHICAL ISSUES

Several environmental ethical issues will be discussed throughout this chapter, and it is important to describe them briefly now.

Waste and Destruction of Natural Resources

For years we have assumed that our natural resources will last forever, that our water, air, oil, minerals, earth, plants, and trees will always be there for us to use and will never be depleted. However, in recent times we have discovered that there is a limit to everything, including our natural resources. Some believe that we are very close to the end of nature. As we willy-nilly cut down trees for use in wood and paper products, for example, we began to realize that our forests were disappearing. When we had oil shortages in 1973, 1998, 1999, and 2000, and Americans were held hostage by the Arab nations, we began to realize that there was only so much oil in the ground and the sea, and that our pumps would not bring up oil forever. As our rainfall diminished along with our water supply, we began to realize that there was a limit to our water as well, and we simply could not overwater our lawns or let water flow down the drains of our sinks, bathtubs, and toilets or we would actually run out of it.

As each of these realizations hit us, we were shocked that the earth's bounty would not last unless we stopped destroying without rebuilding or replanting and unless we began to conserve our precious natural resources. We simply could not continue cutting down trees without planting new ones to take their place. We also had to recycle paper so that not as many trees would be used up to make it. We had to be careful not merely to let water flow but to restrict our use of it. We couldn't just use and misuse our land by destroying it in digging for oil, coal, and other minerals, and we had to be careful not to exhaust its fertility by continuing to plant in the same soil without protecting it and letting it lie fallow.

Exploiting, Misusing, and Polluting the Environment

We also discovered, probably with what first happened to the air in Los Angeles, California, that heavy industrialization and a tremendous proliferation of automobiles polluted the environment so badly that we found it difficult to breathe, grow things, or even to see on particularly smoggy days. We further discovered that such heavy pollution also destroyed the ozone layer that protects the earth against excessive rays of the sun.

Additionally we found that we could not continue to dump our waste in the ground and in the rivers, lakes, and oceans without dire effects on those bodies of water and their inhabitants. If we drilled for oil in the ocean and sprung a leak or had a spill, we could adversely affect the natural and recreational environments surrounding them, including the plants, animals, or fish within them. As our industrialization and technology increased, so did the toxicity of the waste, and we found ourselves burying in the land or dumping in bodies of water very dangerous and poisonous materials, such as strong chemicals, atomic waste, and other dangerous materials that seriously affected our whole environment as well as us its inhabitants.

Exploiting, Abusing, and Destroying Animals

One of the most controversial ethical issues concerning the environment is the question of animal rights and whether we have moral obligations toward animals. These issues encompass destroying animals for food or for parts of their bodies (e.g., furs, skins, or tusks); hunting them for sport; and using them for scientific and other experimentation.

HUNTING AND DESTROYING ANIMALS FOR FOOD AND BODY PARTS. Since human beings are basically carnivores—that is, meat eaters—and have been throughout history, destroying animals for food has been and is quite common. In the past, we hunted animals for food and often used their skins or other parts of their bodies for clothes. Primitive people seemed, however, to use only what they needed and did not destroy whole herds of animals just for the sake of killing them. Hunting for food and other necessities is an ancient activity. Hunting and acquiring food and other items were combined, but early human beings seemed to have more respect for animals and the environment than modern ones do.

Several changes have occurred, however, which some people see as eliminating the necessity of using animals for these purposes. First, we have created wonderful synthetic materials—even furs—that eliminate the need for killing animals for their skins. We no longer need whale blubber in order to operate oil lamps because we now have electricity. We no longer need to hunt animals for food because we now raise animals specifically for the food that we eat (creating another ethical issue that we will discuss later). Killing wild animals, then, has become a sport that many enjoy and many others decry because they feel it amounts to murdering animals for excitement and also threatens to cause certain wild animals to become extinct.

RAISING ANIMALS FOR FOOD. Ethical issues also have arisen with regard to the raising, slaughtering, and eating of animals for food. The demands of modern humans for tastier meats and other animal products, such as eggs, butter, and milk, have caused the food industry to resort to different ways of raising animals for food, some of which cause animals to suffer until they are slaughtered. For example, in the past, animals were raised in the open plains and were allowed to graze, roam, and live in the open air until such time as they were to be slaughtered for food. Nowadays, many animals are raised inside, cooped up in narrow pens, and never allowed outside to graze normally. Some animals never see the sun or breathe the open air, and they are fed food and chemicals that will make them the fattest the soonest without regard for their own likes or dislikes or any concern for their comfort or the pain such conditions or diets may bring.

Some people argue that given what we know about the way animals are raised and about what foods really are good for us, we should stop eating meat at all, thus making the need to raise and slaughter animals for food obsolete. Such people state further that even if we continue to eat meat, we ought to do so sparingly, and, at any rate, we should not use cruel and inhumane methods as we raise animals for this purpose.

USING ANIMALS FOR SCIENTIFIC EXPERIMENTATION. One of the oldest controversies concerning our moral obligations toward animals is whether they should be experimented upon for scientific or medical advancement. Since the antivivisection movement of the nineteenth century protested the cutting into live animals for purposes of scientific research, these protests have expanded to include any experimentation on animals "for the good of humanity." There are strong laws concerning experimenting on human beings, and thus animals must be used, according to science, to test drugs and scientific or medical procedures. Without the use of animals, many of our greatest scientific advancements and cures for diseases (e.g., heart disease, kidney disease, and diabetes) would never have been made. Opponents of animal experimentation argue that often it is totally unnecessary as well as harmful and fatal to the animals being experimented on. They argue that research should be conducted without the use of either humans or animals.

ENDANGERMENT, DECIMATION, AND EXTINCTION OF ANIMAL SPECIES. Because of the encroachment of civilization, as when forests are cut down and towns are built, the natural habitats of animals have shrunk significantly or been destroyed. In addition, because of the continuing demand for animal skins, parts, and trophies, whole species have been slaughtered to the point of extreme endangerment or extinction. Animal rights supporters deplore such activities and have called for an end of the hunting of all animals, especially endangered species, and also for the restriction of any activities that will destroy the environments in which animals live and thrive. They argue that every effort must be made to stop all activities that threaten any animal species, and that attempts should be made to restore such environments to their natural states.

Many issues have arisen in our century that deal with the proper stance people should be taking toward the natural environment and all of its inhabitants. The first important question we should address concerning these issues is what lies behind the attitudes that brought the issues to a head. What caused us to see nature as something to be controlled and manipulated for our own use, regardless of the effects on it and all it contains? Why have we arrived at such a state that we have to be concerned about our relationship with the environment and animals?

OUR ATTITUDE TOWARD NATURE AND WHAT LIES BEHIND IT

Attitudes toward nature have not developed overnight; however, we cannot say that they always have been nor that they always are present in every culture. In the Native American culture, for example, there exists a kind of monistic (oneness) or wholistic view of nature and humanness as being one, not as separate from each other. Native

Americans historically and currently see themselves as a part of nature, as closely related to everything natural rather than as something or someone separate from it. They believe that spirits inhabit everything, not just them, and they relate to nature and animals as if they were family. They take only what they need and have a deep respect for all aspects of nature and animals.

Eastern religions, such as Hinduism, Buddhism, and Taoism, also see nature and humans as being one unified whole instead of seeing nature as subordinate to humans or as something to be manipulated and controlled by them. Here again, unlike Western religions, if spirituality is accepted by the religion, it tends to permeate everyone and everything, not just human beings. The whole universe is spiritual, not just humans and God. The Western view, however, has tended to see humans and nature in a dualistic relationship that is sometimes almost adversarial. There are two major sources in Western culture from which this dualism emerged.

Platonic Dualism: The Beginnings of Western Philosophy

Socrates and then Plato both tended to see the external world as the shadow copy of a real world that exists somewhere else in what Plato called the "world of ideas." With these two men, philosophy moved away from the external world, which had been the focus of the pre-Socratic philosophers (the first scientists), to a focus on human beings and their reason, which enabled them to attain the real world of ideas, a world that Plato felt exists outside of or beyond this world. Both Socrates and Plato, then, tended to deemphasize the importance of this world as opposed to the world of ideas where they felt that ultimate truths could be found, but only through human reason. Plato felt that if human beings concentrated on the external world and everything that was in it, they would only be seeing shadow copies of the real world that exists beyond this world. For example, when Socrates asked a question of his students, such as, "What is justice?" and they answered, "Justice is how Zeus treated Achilles in a certain situation," he then said, "No. I mean what is justice, 'itself by itself'?" In other words, he felt that somewhere there exists the ultimate true idea of justice from which all just acts are mere manifestations. This dualism enabled the Greeks to think abstractly for the first time in their history, but it also tended to split them away from nature in that they, as reasoning beings, saw themselves as different from and more important than nature and the external world, because they and no other beings in nature could attain the "real" world of ideas that Plato thought actually existed.

Judeo-Christian Teachings in the Bible

The second dualistic view emerges from the early Judeo-Christian tradition, which taught that God is a supernatural, spiritual being who shares His spirituality with human beings. No other being in nature, according to the teachings in both traditions, has any spirituality. Again, this world is viewed as being God's creation and significant, but not the real world that lies beyond in the supernatural world (according to Christianity). In Genesis, Adam is told by God that he has "dominion over the animals of the earth, the birds of the air, and the fish of the sea" and that nature essentially is there for his purposes. Adam is told to "go forth and multiply" and have dominion over everything. This again makes nature and everything in it subservient to human beings and their wishes, implying that nature exists strictly for their use and has little or no value in itself. This may not be the way many worshipers in Judaism and Christianity feel today, but there is no doubt that these teachings have had a definite influence on the attitudes people in the Western world have toward nature.

The Rise of Science and Scientific Progress

It is ironic that the influences just mentioned, although giving rise to an exploitative attitude toward nature, also have made science and scientific progress possible. It is no accident that science has progressed by leaps and bounds in the Western world, while being almost nonexistent in the Eastern world. And why not? If nature, and all it contains, is subservient to us, or if we can make it so by harnessing its powers and using it for our own best interest, then why not do so?

As science and technology advanced, nature became more and more subservient to human needs and desires, and the environment and animals were used and exploited without regard to any inherent value they might have. After all, so the attitude went, we are the only beings with intrinsic value; nature has only instrumental value, that is, it is only valuable as it helps us attain whatever goals we believe are important to us.

Industrialization

With the tremendous advancement of science and technology, most nations in the West and many in the East have become highly industrialized, requiring a greater use of natural resources and also causing a greater deleterious effect on the environment because of the need for more land, and air, and a greater disposal of waste. For example, given our civilization's need for certain chemicals or chemical products, a chemical plant may be situated in a natural setting on a river, which requires trees to be cut and hills to be leveled, while the plant pours its poisonous waste into that body of water and pollutes the air by belching chemical-laden smoke into it.

Encroachment of Nature by Civilization

Civilization's encroachment upon nature has also taken many forms. As we have moved out of crowded cities into the countryside nearby and created suburbs, we have eliminated more and more of the natural environment and replaced it with our own. As we have leveled trees and hills to put in housing developments, shopping centers, and other "civilized" creations, we have shrunk the natural environment and pushed species of plant growth and animals back into narrower areas where they often have not been able to survive because of the elimination of their space, air, water, and food supplies.

All of the preceding have contributed to our attitudes toward the natural environment and all it contains. It remains to be seen whether these attitudes should prevail, or whether they should undergo radical or moderate changes. An examination and analysis of the arguments for and against the use and exploitation of nature will help us to look at both sides of environmental ethical issues.

ARGUMENTS FOR USE AND EXPLOITATION OF THE NATURAL ENVIRONMENT

Dominion-over-Nature Arguments

A strong set of arguments states that human beings are the highest form of natural creation and, therefore, should have complete dominion over nature and everything that it contains. Nature exists strictly for the use of human beings and has no other purpose for its existence. These arguments come from two sources: religion and science.

RELIGIOUS BASIS FOR DOMINION. As pointed out, Western religions seem to support the stance that people, although related to nature, are yet other and higher than nature by virtue of the spirituality that has been conferred upon them by God. No other beings in nature have such high status as humans; therefore, they do not deserve the same ethical considerations as humans do. It is strictly up to human beings to decide what the value of nature is, since it has no value in and of itself.

NATURAL ORDER AND EVOLUTION ARGUMENT. The other argument that supports humans' dominion over nature is that which focuses on the evolutionary scale and the natural order of things that places human beings at the top of everything. Humans, by virtue of their fantastic brains that are considered (by them) to be the highest achievement of nature and evolution, should obviously have dominion over everything else in the natural world. Humans have shown through their ability to reason and invent that, even though nature towers over them in size, they are capable of harnessing it and all of its aspects by flying; traveling on and staying under water; controlling rivers, streams, and seas; leveling the tallest mountains; cutting down nature's biggest trees; and overcoming nature's most ferocious species of animals. And even though nature does in some respects have more control over humans (as demonstrated by earthquakes, tornadoes, floods, and tidal waves), it is just a matter of time until humans will be able to control these aspects of nature too by being able to predict them and then by either averting them or diminishing their destructive powers.

Human Reasoning versus Nature as Blind and Nonreasoning

The main reason that human beings are at the top of the natural order of things is that they have the capacity for reasoning that the rest of nature does not possess. Inanimate objects and plants have no reasoning ability, and animals have it to only a minor degree, if at all. Because nature is blind and nonreasoning, it is obvious that human beings should have complete dominion and control over it.

Civilization More Important Than Nature

Because the human brain and its reasoning capacity is the highest form in the natural order, then civilization, including its institutions, technology, science, industry, and systems of all kinds, should take precedence over nature. Neither nature nor any of its inhabitants except for human beings are capable of reasoning, analyzing, organizing, using a language, or creating. Therefore, if nature must be destroyed in order to allow human civilization to expand and progress, then it simply must be, as it is less important in all of its aspects.

Moral Rights and Obligations

Because humans are at the top of the religious and natural orders, they and only they are deserving of moral rights and obligations; therefore, we have moral obligations only to ourselves and other human beings and not to nature in any of its aspects. Morality does not exist as far as the rest of nature is concerned but either comes from God or is established by humans for humans; therefore, humans have no moral obligations toward any part of nature nor does any part of nature have any moral rights. Nature, then, can be used and exploited in any way that humans see fit, for it is merely there for their purposes.

ARGUMENTS AGAINST THE USE AND EXPLOITATION OF NATURE

Monistic Wholism versus Dominion and Domination

Critics of the dualistic arguments that human beings and nature are separate and that the former have been given dominion over the latter state that, first, religious arguments either have been misinterpreted or are irrelevant. Since nature is part of God's creation, say some religionists, it also should be treated with respect. Just because there are no souls in nonhumans doesn't mean they have no value whatsoever. Second, having dominion, as given by God, means that humans should treat nature as God treats humans, with respect, mercy, and love. If humans are rulers over the world, then they should be benevolent and care for those beings under their rule who do not have the great human capacity for reason.

Also, some passages in the King James version of the Bible could be interpreted as supporting acting morally rather than destructively or dominatingly toward nature.

THE OLD TESTAMENT. First, in the Old Testament in Genesis, Chapter 9, Verses 12 and 15, it would seem that God made His covenant with Noah to include not only human beings but also animals:

> *Verse 12:* *And God said, "This is the token of the covenant which I make between me and you and every living creature that is with you for perpetual generations."*
>
> *Verse 15:* *"And I will remember my covenant, which is between me and you and every living creature of all flesh; and the waters shall no more become a flood to destroy all flesh."*

THE NEW TESTAMENT. Second, in the New Testament in Revelation, Chapters 7 and 9, God again seems to express some concern for the nature He created:

> *Chapter 7, Verses 2 and 3:* *And I saw another angel ascending from the east, having the seal of the living God, and he cried with a loud voice to the four angels, to whom it was given to hurt earth and sea, saying, "Hurt not the earth, neither the sea, nor the trees, till we have sealed a hundred and forty and four thousand of all the tribes of the children of Israel."*
>
> *Chapter 9, Verses 3 and 4:* *And there came out of the smoke locusts upon the earth; and unto them was given power, as the scorpions of the earth have power. And it was commanded them that they should not hurt the grass of the earth, neither any green thing, neither any tree; but only those men which have not the seal of God in their foreheads.*

Nonreligionists argue that, first, just because people have evolved as higher beings because of their brains doesn't mean that someday they won't be replaced by a yet higher species. Second, this argument does not mean that nature is inferior to, but rather that it is equal to them in every respect. The proper relationship between humans and nature is not dualistic, but wholistic; that is, human beings are an integral part of nature and nature is an integral part of them. Therefore, instead of being a relationship of "survival of the fittest" or domination of one species over all the rest, this relationship should be a reciprocal and wholistic one. The relationship should be one in which all aspects are a part of the whole of nature, to be preserved and protected and to coexist in harmony.

Reasoning Should Not Separate Humans from Nature

Because humans can reason, they should realize that nature is intrinsically valuable and must be nurtured and related to in a meaningful manner. Reason should not cause humans to reject nature, but to prize it; as a matter of fact, having reason endows humans with much more responsibility toward nature and all it contains than other beings in nature who do not possess it. Where animals are concerned, the importance of reasoning should be expanded to include sentientism (having mental states) so that animals can be respected even though they cannot reason. There are also certain criteria put forth by some ethicists that clearly can be used to give rights to animals and require human obligations toward them (see the following section on "Criteria for Animal Rights").

CIVILIZATION VERSUS NATURE.   Nature, which contains most human needs and which relates to humans in a vital way, should never be made subordinate to civilization, which is human constructed. Civilization has its value and importance, but nature should never be seriously endangered or destroyed at the expense of expanding civilization. For example, when builders are contemplating putting up a housing development or other buildings, they should never destroy any part of the natural environment in which they are working. Plant and animal life must be preserved and not destroyed as designing and building take place. Frank Lloyd Wright (1869–1959), the great American architect and advocate of organic architecture, believed that buildings should be designed in such a way that they fit into the natural environment or even seem to emerge from it in an organic way. His famous cantilevered house at Willow Run is a perfect example of this attitude.

MODERATE POSITION

Both of the preceding sets of arguments take extreme positions either for or against the use and exploitation of nature. The arguments for such use and exploitation advocate the total subordination of nature to humans and the free use and exploitation of nature for whatever reasons humans deem acceptable. On the other hand, the arguments against these suggest that nature must be considered as standing on an equal footing with humans and should never be used as a means to human ends (see Kant's Practical Imperative). A more moderate position exists between these two extremes, however, one in which nature generally is regarded as being important and significant, but not necessarily on the same footing with humans, and in which it may be used for human means with some care so as not to seriously endanger or destroy it.

This position generally agrees with the wholistic position, seeing nature and humans as being intimately related and requiring that humans treat nature with respect; however, it is not against using nature for the good of humans but insists that this be done carefully, allowing for the preservation and protection of the environment and animals in the process and being careful not to overuse either of these. Perhaps these three positions dealing with humans and their relationship to nature can be best exemplified through a discussion of animal rights and human moral obligations toward animals.

CRITERIA FOR ANIMAL RIGHTS

Life and Being Alive

Some might argue that as long as something has life or is alive, it deserves moral consideration, and people have a moral obligation to protect and preserve life wherever it is found. Critics of this position say that it is much too vague and unrealistic and that it would seem to violate the way nature itself works. A food chain exists in nature in which plants feed on other plants, animals feed on plants, and animals feed on other animals. Nature is able to achieve a balance in this process in which species survive but do not necessarily become extinct because they are not destroyed through overhunting, overeating, or overkilling.

Human beings also make distinctions concerning whether just life and being alive constitute sufficient criteria to preserve life. They have and do follow nature in that they eat plants and animals for their own survival just as the latter do for theirs. Further, humans even allow the killing of their own species in certain instances. Even though these are controversial areas, humans do allow the termination of life in their own species in such cases as abortion, defense of the innocent, capital punishment, just wars, mercy death, and mercy killing. If humans allow this in their own species, why not in others as well, especially if it is clearly for the good of the human species? Therefore, the fact that something or someone merely is alive or has life does not in itself seem to constitute a strong argument against terminating that life for this or that good reason.

Having Interests

Joel Feinberg states that "to have a right is to have a claim to something and *against* someone," and goes on to say that only beings who can be said to have interests are capable of claiming such rights.[1] He considers that animals do have interests, even though they can't express them verbally, especially the interest not to suffer pain, and therefore he would argue that animals do indeed have rights.

Attributes of Soul, Mind, and Feelings

Some would argue that rights for moral treatment are based upon whether a being has a soul, a mind, or feelings. The difficulty of proving the existence or nonexistence of a soul creates problems with such a criterion. Furthermore, even if we could prove a soul's existence, why should that be the only claim to moral rights?

As far as mind and feelings are concerned, animals, as sentient beings like humans, have to be described as having both of these merely through our observation of them. It seems obvious that they have sense experiences, although often different from those of humans, and they seem to be able to express sadness, happiness, and anger as well as other emotions and states of consciousness (e.g., conscious awareness and response to stimuli).

Reason

Although it is limited, animals do seem to also have an ability to reason, even if only on a rudimentary level. Current language experiments with chimpanzees and gorillas would seem to indicate this. Furthermore, human beings with severe mental impairment can reason at no higher a level than some animals do, and generally we give them rights and feel we have moral obligations toward them; therefore, why do we not also have such obligations toward animals? It would seem that the mere fact of being sentient (having mental states) in itself would elicit from us humans at least the obligation not to inflict pain and suffering on one who is so.

WAYS OF DEALING WITH ANIMAL RIGHTS

Vegetarianism

One way of ensuring animal rights is to avoid using animals for food at all and to eat only vegetables. In this way, hunting or slaughtering animals for food no longer becomes necessary. There are many kinds of people who call themselves vegetarians—some who will not eat any meat at all, some who will eat only poultry and fish, and some who will not even eat animal products such as dairy and eggs. These latter are called "vegans." Some extremists, such as the Jainists, will not even eat vegetables from plants that have to be killed to yield the fruit or vegetable, such as potatoes. They will themselves not kill plants to eat their food but will wait until food drops from plants or trees or accept food donations from others who will pick them.

It is often difficult to attain some consistency as we try to preserve the lives of plants and animals. For example, what is the difference, beyond the health reasons, between eating red meat and eating poultry or fish? Is it any more moral to kill and eat a chicken or a fish than it is to kill and eat a cow or sheep?

Arguments Against Vegetarianism

Some argue that even though animals have interests and rights, those interests and rights are of less importance than those of humans, and therefore we have a right to use them for food, just as animals in nature use other animals and vegetables for food. The moderate view states that with these rights go certain responsibilities not to make animals suffer or feel pain, or not to slaughter whole species and make them extinct, but that humans still are entitled to kill animals for food within these moral limitations.

Sentientism

A second way of dealing with animal rights is to respect the fact that they have mental states that are to some extent akin to those of humans and are therefore deserving of rights. The critics of this argument ask, "What about plants and trees?" Sentientism is too restrictive and ignores the livingness of nonanimals. Don't our forests and fields deserve the same kind of consideration as any other living being? These people generally argue for wholism.

Wholism

Every living thing is deserving of respect according to this view because humans, animals, and plants are part of a natural whole and must learn to live in harmony with one another. This attitude relies heavily upon human beings and their reasoning, especially moral reasoning. The critics of this view argue against the blurring of important distinctions between humans, animals, and plants and state that there is indeed a hierarchy of beings that allows us to deem the rights of certain beings to be more important than others'. For example, animal rights activists are more concerned about animals than they are about plants and feel that animals should be given more consideration than wholism would allow.

USE OF ANIMALS FOR FOOD

One of the most important issues, because of its prevalency, is the raising and slaughtering of animals for food. Is it moral to kill sentient beings, possessing all of the attributes described previously, and use them for human consumption? There are people who stand on both sides of this issue and some who are in the middle. What is involved in both the raising and the slaughtering of animals for this purpose?

Ways of Raising Animals for Food

In the past, wild animals were hunted and their flesh was used for food, while their skins or other body parts were used for clothes and other items. When humans became more civilized, they began to domesticate animals, such as cows, pigs, sheep, and chickens, and to raise them for food. Animals were raised in the open air on farms or ranches alongside one or both of their parents, allowed to graze in pastures, or fed corn or other grains or foods while sometimes being penned in the open air. This is called the "free-range" system of raising animals for food. When the time came for slaughter, the animals generally were put to death as quickly and as painlessly as possible.

However, as the demand for more and better meat and other animal products increased, something called "factory farming" came into use. Animals are raised in very close pens, often in the dark, and few of them ever see their mothers or the light of day. Even though killing animals for food is considered to be immoral by some, under the old system, they at least were treated more or less humanely up to the time of slaughter. An example of what goes on in factory farming can be seen in a description of how calves are raised for the veal that humans eat:

> In order to make their flesh pale and tender, these calves are given special treatment. They are put in narrow stalls and tethered with a chain so that they cannot turn around, lie down comfortably, or groom themselves. They are fed a totally liquid diet to promote rapid weight gain. This diet is deficient in iron and, as a result, the calves lick the sides of the stall, which are impregnated with urine containing iron. They are given no water because thirsty animals eat more than those who drink water. Is this cruel treatment morally justified? Should we do this to animals just because we enjoy eating their flesh?[2]

A similar description could be given with regard to the raising of chickens, lambs, or pigs and also to using animals for their products, such as eggs, milk, and cream. Is this moral?

The Vegetarian Position

Because vegetarians oppose using animals for food in any way, shape, or form, such people would be totally against the factory farming way of raising animals, calling it even more decadent and corrupt than raising animals on the open farms as before. To raise and kill animals strictly for our needs is to use living, sentient beings merely as a means to our own ends without even the kindness of letting them have a relatively happy and good life before we kill them.

The Carnivore Position

The carnivore or meat-eating position accepts this approach as a modernized and much more efficient way of giving humans the best-quality food possible. Because animals are here basically for our use and have no intrinsic value, we have no moral obligations toward them, and their suffering has no meaning, since they are less than human. Therefore, any method that brings humans the best quality of meat possible is morally acceptable regardless of how it affects the animals involved.

The Moderate Position

The moderate position might condone using animals for food but decry the factory farming method as cruel. It would state that animals may be used by humans for food but insist on the free-range method of raising them and their painless slaughter as basic requirements for dealing morally with them. It would not, of course, deny the rights of vegetarians, but it would not brand as immoral the eating of meat aside from the cruelty to animals in the process of raising or slaughtering them.

USE OF ANIMALS FOR EXPERIMENTATION

The use of animals for experimentation has gone on for many years and has resulted in the development of many of the greatest scientific and medical discoveries that have helped people to rid themselves of all kinds of chronic and fatal diseases.

Arguments for Animal Experimentation

Scientists would argue that without the ability to use animals for experimentation, humans would have to be used, to their harm and sometimes fatality. Cures simply would not be found for diseases, nor would training in certain procedures, such as surgeries, be possible. Because by law humans cannot be used for experimentation without their informed consent and without tremendous safeguards being imposed, progress in science and medicine simply would have to come to a standstill if animals could not be used.

They would argue further that animals have much less value than human beings, so it is morally correct to use them for experimentation because what will be discovered will benefit many people and sometimes the whole of humankind. Many of the animals scientists use are merely put to death because no one wants them and they cannot be kept in pounds or animal shelters indefinitely; therefore, why not get some use out of them rather than just kill them? The mere fact that nobody wants them or will take care of them should make it all right to use them to benefit humans.

Arguments Against Using Animals for Experimentation

In the view of animal rights activists, animals are thinking, feeling beings that suffer pain to the same extent and degree as humans. Just because they cannot tell us how much what is being done to them hurts doesn't mean they don't feel the pain. Therefore, it is immoral to put animals through suffering, torture, and painful death just so that humans can make progress in science and medicine. Even though Kant's Practical Imperative was meant to apply to rational human beings, animal rights activists would apply it to animals, giving them the same rights and status as human beings.

Many experiments are absolutely unnecessary to the health and well-being of human beings, and yet experiments continue to put animals through terrible tortures and death, merely in order to satisfy scientific curiosity. For example,

> At the Lovelace Foundation in New Mexico, experimenters forced sixty-four beagles to inhale radioactive strontium 90. Twenty-five of the dogs died; initially most of them were feverish and anemic and had hemorrhages and bloody diarrhea. One of the deaths occurred during an epileptic seizure, and another resulted from a brain hemorrhage. In a similar experiment, beagles were injected with enough strontium 90 to produce early death in fifty percent of the group. . . . It was already known that strontium 90 was unhealthy, and that the dogs would suffer and die. Furthermore, these experiments did not save any human lives or have any important benefits for humans.[3]

Animal rights activists see absolutely no redeeming moral value in such experiments and in fact deem them to be terribly immoral. Even when the outcome of experiments is such as to help scientists fight human diseases, other methods besides using animals merely as a means to our own ends must be found, or scientific progress simply should not be made. It is immoral, in these activists' eyes, to use animals for such purposes regardless of how much it may help mankind.

Moderate Position

The moderate position would not be against using animals for experimentation, but it would insist that, first of all, experiments must be absolutely necessary to the health and well-being of human beings. Animals should never be experimented upon merely to satisfy human curiosity, nor should they ever be used for unnecessary experiments such as that described with the beagles.

Second, every care must be taken to avoid inflicting upon animals more pain and suffering during the experiment than is actually needed. Every effort must be made to keep animals out of pain while experiments are going on, and they should be given almost the same amount of respect that would be tendered toward our fellow humans. With these safeguards in mind, necessary animal experimentation may be done.

KILLING ANIMALS FOR SPORT

It Should Be Allowed

AN ANCIENT ACTIVITY OF MAN.   Several arguments exist for killing animals for sport. Hunting animals was an ancient activity of men in many of the tribes and cultures of the past and it remains so in cultures of the present. Some would argue that it is a part of manhood to engage in the hunting and killing of animals for food, skins, trophies, or just for the thrill of the hunt.

CONTROLLING ANIMAL POPULATION.   Protagonists of this position would argue that killing animals at will is the only way of keeping the animal population under control. As humans have built ranches and farms farther into the natural environment, wild animals often have attacked their crops or their domestic animals that are raised for food or for commercial reasons. Such animals must be trapped and killed so as to preserve civilization. If the hunting of wild animals is not allowed, even the least ferocious of them will destroy crops and domestic animals. Further, they will overrun our farms, ranches, and even our towns and cities, especially where there are suburbs. Therefore, in order to keep the animal population under control, hunting should not merely be allowed but encouraged.

DESIRE FOR ANIMAL MEAT AND OTHER BODY PARTS.   First, despite the fact that we have all the domestic meat we may wish, many people like to eat wild game, such as duck, venison (deer meat), quail, and pheasant, and they should be allowed to indulge their tastes.

Second, many people like to use the skins of wild animals of all kinds to make clothes, shoes, boots, handbags, floor coverings, and wall hangings. Even though all of these items can be made from synthetic materials or from domestic animals' skins, the more exotic wild skins are often prettier, rarer, and valued more highly. It is one thing, for example, to own a pair of cowboy boots made of cowhide, but another to own a pair made from lizard, crocodile, porcupine, or rattlesnake hides. The higher prices for boots made from these skins attest to their higher value.

Third, it is exciting to be able to have the heads of wild animals one has hunted and killed in the jungles and forests hanging on one's walls to indicate prowess and bravery as a hunter. And it is fun and different to have a wastebasket made of an elephant's foot, carved ivory figures made from its tusks, and coats and capes made from the beautiful skins and furs of real wild animals. Some people play tennis, swim, or ski for sport, so why shouldn't the hunter or fisherman be allowed to pursue his or her own preferred sport?

It Should Not Be Allowed

AN ANCIENT ACTIVITY NO LONGER REQUIRED.   The very fact that hunting is an ancient activity should indicate that it is not necessarily needed in modern times. We no longer have the need for the meat, skins, or body parts of wild animals. Furthermore, modern civilized males should not need to prove their masculinity at the expense of innocent and often beautiful animals who do nothing to harm them and who should be allowed to roam free as they once did.

THE ANIMAL POPULATION WILL CONTROL ITSELF.   The major cause of the increase in the animal population is that humans have hunted and killed carnivores such as mountain lions, wolves, and bobcats. These predators used to hunt and eat animals such as deer and rabbits, thereby naturally keeping the animal population under control. If hunting these animals were no longer allowed, then the animals they hunt would become a menace as indeed they have. If this natural control system cannot be, then there must be more humane ways of controlling animal populations other than shooting them for sport.

NO FURTHER NEED FOR WILD GAME OR BODY PARTS.   It is a decadent civilization, antagonists to hunting as a sport would say, that needs to hunt animals for their meat when perfectly good domestic meat exists for human consumption. In addition, to use animals' body parts, such as their skins, when there are perfectly good synthetic, man-made materials we can use for these purposes is indefensible. We can make synthetic fur coats that look as if they are made of real furs and that do not require us to kill animals for them. The days of using wild animal skins and hides are over, or should be, and there is absolutely no need to kill 50 lizards, for example, in order to make a pair of cowboy boots or club to death hundreds of baby harp seals in order to make fur coats for women. It is the height of decadence that members of a civilized world have to continue to hunt and kill beautiful wild animals for these purposes.

The Moderate Position

KILLING FOR SPORT CAN BE ALLOWED ON A LIMITED BASIS.   We must recognize that other sports, such as skiing and swimming, do not involve the killing of innocent animals. This position recognizes the enjoyment some people get from the hunt and will allow hunting for sport on a limited basis as long as animals, especially endangered species, generally are protected and that there are limits on the type, age, and sex of the animal to be hunted. The hunt must be a fair one, allowing animals to try to save themselves. "Shooting fish in a barrel," as the saying goes, should not be allowed, and poachers should be fined or otherwise heavily penalized.

There should be specific seasons set aside by forest rangers and other officials, and rules protecting animals from extinction should be strictly enforced. Also, until the predator population can be expanded, hunting should coincide with the need for control of populations of "huntable" animals. Here again, strict limits must be enforced so as to ensure that there is no extinction of any species.

NO REASON TO KILL WILD ANIMALS FOR MEAT.   Except where hunting is allowed, as described, no hunting outside of established limits should take place for meat or body parts unless it is done by primitive tribes in order to get meat for their villages when no other meat can be acquired.

NO KILLING ANIMALS FOR BODY PARTS AND SKINS.   Again, except where allowed within the limits described, no hunting should take place to acquire animal body parts, such as heads for trophies, skins or furs for clothes and footwear, feet for wastebaskets, or tusks for ivory. In order to help ensure that this type of hunting stops, civilized people should not demand such items and should make a strong effort not to order or purchase them; they should openly declare their opposition to such wasteful and useless hunting. In other words, every effort should be made to restrict hunting to a minimum.

PROTECTION OF ENDANGERED SPECIES

People who are not particularly concerned about the extinction of species of animals, especially exotic species, cannot see what all the fuss is about. Why worry about such things? Nature always has allowed various species to become extinct; perhaps it is now occurring by means of the advancement of human beings and their civilization. Why, for example, should people try to preserve the California condor? It is one of the ugliest birds in existence and basically is a carrion or vulturelike bird feeding off the carcasses of dead animals. Why does it matter whether we save such species or even those that are prettier to look at? There are several arguments that animal protectionists bring up regarding endangered species:

1. An irreverence for even a small segment of life affects one's reverence for all life. If one has no consideration for even one species, then he or she is likely not to have consideration for any other, including his own. Protectionists argue that human beings should protect and preserve all viable life in all of its forms, not just human life, as best they can.
2. Most species of animals are beautiful or at least interesting to see and know about, especially in their natural habitats, so they should be available not only for us but also for our children, grandchildren, and great-grandchildren. If we are not careful about encroaching upon animals' habitats and destroying them in all the ways we can and do, then there will be fewer and fewer species around for us and our kin to experience.
3. All animals seem to contribute in some way to the balance of nature and to the natural food chain. We may not clearly know how everything fits into the overall plan of nature, but we should be careful not to upset the balance any more than we have to. It is one thing for nature to take its course and to make certain species extinct, but whenever it is obvious that humans, not nature, are the cause of destruction or extinction, we should cease what we are doing, or do what we are doing less, so as not to affect nature and its inhabitants adversely.

These are the reasons animal protectionists give for doing our utmost to protect and preserve all species of animals, and especially those that are becoming endangered. Obviously such people would be totally against hunting any of these species and also would tend to want to curtail the progress and encroachment of civilization upon nature wherever it tends to threaten the existence of such species.

NON-WESTERN PERSPECTIVES ON ENVIRONMENTAL ISSUES

Because environmental problems are global in scope and implications raised by these important issues of concern affect people the world over, it will be worthwhile to briefly note the value of non-Western ethical viewpoints. Asian values offer productive alternatives to rights-based moralities that dominate Western societies. There has been much recent debate concerning Asian values, and one is led to assume that there is one distinct set of values common to all Asians. This assumption is surely false and misleading, because Asia covers a huge geographical area and Asian traditions include Daoist,

Confucian, Buddhist, Neo-Confucian, Hindu, and Jain values. Furthermore, Roman Catholicism is the dominant religion in the Philippines, and Islam is widespread in Pakistan and Indonesia. So when we talk of the values of Asia, it becomes obvious that there is a plurality of ethical thought systems that could be included for discussion. However, four Asian ethical traditions, two originating in India and two in China, seem especially well suited to addressing environmental issues.

Ethical Traditions of South Asia: Hinduism and Buddhism

The fundamental aim of philosophical thinking in India and the ethical traditions of South Asia is to bring about liberation from all suffering. The immanent worldviews of Hinduism and Buddhism, which stress the oneness and interconnectedness of the natural order, present clear alternatives to Western transcendent moral perspectives where human beings stand over/against nature. Also, there is no clear distinction between the sacred and the profane, because philosophy in India is not separated from religious activity. Wisdom in South Asian cultures is wholistic in nature and is manifest as knowledge and compassion. "True wisdom is the harmony of mind and heart."[4] For the Hindu "all is one." As one scholar states, "Oneness is not the one word to describe the essence of Hinduism, but it is as close as we can get to a one-word characterization."[5] This fundamental principle is expressed as the truth that *atman* (the individual soul) is *Brahman* (the world soul). Ignorance of this insight leads to the illusion of a separate existence standing over/against its ground. This failure to apprehend the most basic truth about the nature of self and the nature of the universe constitutes the major reason for bondage, misery, and destruction in the world. The goal of Hinduism thus is to gain a discriminatory self-transforming knowledge of reality. Acting in the light of this knowledge has a liberating effect upon all existence.

Right conduct for the Hindu is understood in terms of the concept of *dharma*. This notion is derived from the root *dhr,* meaning "to nourish." The term's etymology may be further traced to the word *rita*—the order of the universe. *Dharma* is action that is selfless and without attachment, thus it promotes the oneness and wholeness of all things. Hindus believe that moral order permeates all existence. This idea is played out in the notion of *karma*—the law of sowing and reaping or the principle of moral cause and effect. How is *rita* "the moral order of the universe" related to human actions and their consequences? Hindu scholar Saral Jhingran tells us that

> the moral quality of our deeds, thoughts and desires not only conditions our future character, but also manipulates the natural world order, so that we are thrown into external circumstances that are most suited to materialize or effect the kind of rewards and punishments which our moral character deserves.[6]

"Right conduct," *dharma*, requires that one take responsibility for one's deeds and thoughts in ways that lead to "personal self-realization," *moksha*, and at the same time nourishes society and existence itself.

Buddhism shares the basic Hindu cosmology and places emphasis on the interconnectedness of all things. According to Buddhist teaching, all things are intimately connected in the sense that they affect everything else. Like the ecological system itself, existence is an intricate, interdependent web within which all cause-and-effect relationships occur. In light of this insight one may conclude that, likewise, all human actions impact all other things. Such a metaphysical scheme frames ethical thinking in terms of global accountability.

Buddhist doctrine also emphasizes the Noble Truth of Suffering. That "life is suffering (*duhkha*)" is the central truth of Buddhism and the Buddha's estimate of the world condition. The goal of Buddhist teaching and practice is to achieve nirvana, liberation from suffering (*duhkha*) and release from the cycle of rebirth. Suffering (*duhkha*) is brought about by ignorance. On the one hand, many wrongly identify existence with being and thus experience *duhkha* as a result of attachments to this world and the things of the world. On the other hand, others misidentify existence with nonbeing and, as a consequence, experience *duhkha* in the rejection of life. Although Buddhism teaches the doctrine of "No Self," which is the denial of the self or ego as a separate and permanent entity, it does not deny self as a concrete, living, dynamic entity. Life on Buddhist terms is a process and is constantly changing, yet every moment holds within itself both being and nonbeing. Right living consists in following the Middle Way—the path between a life of attachment (and the extremes of self-indulgence and greed) and the rejection of life and self-denial or deprivation.

The Middle Way is articulated as The Eightfold Path:

- right view (knowledge)
- right intention (resolve)
- right speech
- right conduct
- right livelihood
- right effort
- right mindfulness
- right concentration

Relative to the preceding eight points, one must negotiate the balance between the extremes of materialism and its attachments and ritualism which denies the value of material existence. Since the goal of Buddhism is to liberate all sentient beings from suffering, right living stresses the primary of the virtue of compassion.

Ethical Traditions of East Asia: Daoism and Confucianism

The grand goal of Chinese thought is to achieve balance and harmony. Both Daoism and Confucianism presuppose a dynamic, aesthetically ordered, *yin-yang* constitutive cosmos. *Yin-yang* originally referred to the shaded and the sunny, and the two notions represent complementary, interpenetrating opposites, reciprocals, or counterpoints that move around the still point of the universe and account for change. Examples of *yin* would include dark, female, wet, and soft, while illustrations of *yang* are light, male, dry, and hard. In a Chinese world, harmony and balance are sought between other *yin/yang counterpoints*: heaven and earth, intuition and reason, others and self, and nature and society. Because Daoism is chiefly identified with nature and Confucianism with society, the two are sometimes said to represent the *yin* and *yang* of Chinese thought.

Daoist thought is embodied in the person of Laozi, to whom is attributed the philosophical classic, the *Daodejing*—roughly translated, *The Book of the Way and Virtue*. Although it is doubtful that such an individual actually existed, tradition suggests he was an older contemporary of Kongzi (Confucius) and lived in the sixth century B.C. This book is the Daoist "Bible" and is the chief source for later Daoist writers, such as Zhaungzi (fourth century B.C.). It is the primary source for the entire Daoist canon. It is also the philosophical basis for the Daoist religion and figures significantly in traditional Chinese medicine, the martial arts, and Feng-Shui.

In Daoist thought the key concept is the *dao*—"the way." It refers to the way of ultimate reality. It is also the way of nature and, ethically, it is the way an individual ought to live. In other words, one ought to gear his or her life to the power and rhythms of the *dao*. One ought to live in harmony with nature. Because the *dao* is all pervasive it eliminates the source of all conflict and strife by flowing through and embracing all things. The *Daodejing* teaches that no living being can transgress its natural limits without upsetting the balance of the *dao*. Thus, the Daoist attempts to live in harmony with the underlying patterns that are the source of nature and charge.

Chapter 25 of the *Daodejing* illustrates the harmonious relationships we have been discussing:

> There is something undefined and complete, coming into existence before
>> Heaven and Earth.
>> How still it was and formless, standing alone, and undergoing no
> change,
>> reaching everywhere and in no danger (of being exhausted).
>> It may be regarded as the Mother of all things.
>> I do not know its name,
>> and I give it the designation of the Tao (the Way or Course).
>> Making an effort (further) to give it a name I call it The Great.
>> Great, it passes on (in constant flow).
>> Passing on, it becomes remote.
>> Having become remote, it returns.
>> Therefore the Tao is great;
>> Heaven is great;
>> Earth is great;
>> and the (sage) king is also great.
>> In the universe are four that are great, and the (sage) king is one of them.
>> Man takes his law from the Earth;
>> the Earth takes its law from Heaven;
>> Heaven takes its law from the Tao.
>> The law of the Tao is its being what it is.[7]

Unfortunately, ethically unchecked desire leads to the pursuit of excessive wealth, power, and artificial goods. As a result the natural balance is upset and so is the well-being of the individual, society, other creatures, and larger biological systems. Natural resources are exploited for personal gain or ravaged in a mad rush to secure corporate profits. Daoist wisdom teaches that such unnatural and excessive desires never lead to a satisfying, fulfilled life and are destructive of the very processes that sustain life.

Kongzi (Confucius) was concerned to establish social structures and conventions that would ensure right conduct—conduct that would promote harmony with the *dao*.

Kongzi, in dealing with the human world, attempted to ground his philosophy in the natural order of things. He reasoned that human beings, *by nature*, are social beings. Human beings, he concluded, are nourished, cared for, and flourish best within the structure of the family as governed by the Five Cardinal Relationships. This notion of the family is extended to the entire nation and all relationships are governed by the virtues *ren*—"humanness," "goodness," "human heartedness," or "humaneness"; *li*—"ritual propriety" or "appropriateness" as defined by rites and ritual; and *shu*—"reciprocity" or "mutual consideration." By way of the virtue *li*, Kongzi ritualized proper conduct and life which, in effect, became a performance designed to further the natural harmony. According to Master Kong, "Achieving harmony is the most valuable function of observing ritual propriety."[8]

The difference in both the focus and emphasis of distinct cultural views with respect to environmental ethics offers opportunities for mutual benefit, learning, and enrichment by opening up the scope of the dialogue. In a world of pluralistic cultural values an expanded field of possibilities makes room for alternative responses to serious environmental challenges that are not easily resolved within the limitations of a single cultural viewpoint.

CONCLUSION

As has been the case with most of the moral issues presented in this book, diligent effort has been made to present as fairly as possible the extreme pro and con positions. In some cases moderate positions were also presented. Perhaps the most important question we are left with, after contemplating the moral issues connected with the natural environment, is to what extent it is possible for a balance to be achieved between civilization and its progress and the natural environment and all it contains. Civilization in and of itself is not a bad thing. Human beings have had magnificent achievements through their civilization; at times they have even worked ingeniously to preserve what is best in nature. People who argue for such preservation feel that human beings must never forget that they come from and are a part of nature and that they must always treat it with respect. To the extent that they do not, they will eventually only hurt themselves as well as all the living beings around them.

Cases for Study and Discussion

CASE 1 Seal Hunting

Every year in order to satisfy the demands for seal fur coats, hundreds, even thousands, of baby harp seals are bashed to death on the ice by groups of villagers for whom the sale of such animal skins is the major industry of their village. What occurs is a bloody massacre of a large part of the seal community. Animal rights activists decry this wholesale slaughter of an animal species that is quite innocent and that does not endanger anyone's life. Such slaughter takes place for the sole purpose of satisfying female vanity throughout the "civilized" world when perfectly good synthetic furs could serve the same purpose. The villagers, on the other hand, make their living basically by killing the baby seals and probably would live in poverty if they didn't have this particular business activity. This issue could be extended to include many other animals as well. If you know of other species involved in such "harvesting," present the problem and answer the following questions for that issue also. Do you think that what the villagers are doing is morally right? Why or why not? Can the needs of the villagers be balanced against the lives of the seals? How? What solution to this problem would you suggest?

CASE 2 Killing Animals for Furs

In an Ann Landers column, an upset woman wrote in because someone had criticized her for wearing a rabbit fur coat. She had been asked, "I wonder how many beautiful rabbits died so you could have that coat?" The woman noticed that her questioner was wearing a down coat and retorted, "Do you think the geese they got the down from which to make your coat are still alive?" Ann Landers stated that most of the fur produced in North America is from animals raised on family farms and added that in her opinion it is no more cruel to kill animals for their fur than it is to kill them for food or their hides. She wondered further whether critics of killing animals for fur would be willing to give up their shoes, belts, handbags, saddles, and luggage and any meat they might eat at meals.[9] What do you think of these statements and questions? Is the killing of animals any more justified for food, hides, or feathers than it is for furs? Why or why not? Support your answers in detail. Does it make any difference whether animals are raised on family farms or trapped in the wild? Why or why not? Is there any way to be consistent or to justify inconsistencies when it comes to the use of animals for food, hides, feathers, or furs? For example, someone wrote a letter to the editor of a newspaper stating that the setting on fire by the Animal Liberation Front of a store that sold animal furs is no more justified than setting a restaurant on fire for killing and cooking chickens. How would you sort out and differentiate these issues? Explain in detail.

CASE 3 Oil Spills

A major oil corporation constantly advertises in newspapers, magazines, and on radio and television about what it is doing to protect the environment and endangered species. At the same time, it is responsible for oil spills caused by carelessness both on land and at sea, which, of course, destroy all kinds of sea life and animals that live there. When such spills occur, unless they happen to hit the newspapers because they cannot be hidden from public view, employees are told to clean up the spills, but not to tell anyone outside of the company or even inside the company who does not already know about it. This, of course, would seem to be hypocrisy of the worst kind. Do you think the oil company should spend more time and money on preventing oil spills than on building shelters for some endangered species? Why or why not? What would make the company less hypocritical? Answer in detail. Should the company keep such spills secret when they are unknown to the public, or does it owe the public the right to have that information as well as the advertisements about what they're doing to protect the environment? Why or why not? Is it all right to keep such spills secret because it's good for business? Why or why not?

CASE 4 Animal Testing and Cosmetics

A certain company that manufactures cosmetics uses rabbits to test the irritancy level of its products to their eyes for purposes of making nonirritating cosmetics for the eyes of women who will use such cosmetics. Large doses of any substance to be used are injected into one eye of the rabbits, while the other eye is left alone for comparison of any damage done. The test is painful, and anesthetics are not used on rabbits. Since large doses have to be used in order to provide a greater margin of safety for possible eventual use on humans, permanent eye damage often occurs. No tests that avoid using animals have ever been developed. Is this type of testing moral? Why, or why not? Would the use of rabbits for this purpose be more morally acceptable if they were given painkillers? Why, or why not? Since the products are to be used on humans, should the company ask for human volunteers with the same safeguards being required as for other types of human experimentation? Why, or why not? Do you think animal experimentation is more morally justifiable if it's done for medical reasons—for example, to find a pain relief medication or cure for certain diseases? Why, or why not?

CASE 5 Extinction of Small Fish

A dam was proposed to be built on a certain river in a natural setting that would produce hydroelectric power and create recreational activities, such as boating, swimming, and waterskiing. The only problem, as environmentalists see it, is that there is a certain species of small fish found only in this river that will become extinct if the dam is built. The fish is not used for food or sport; in fact, no one knows what purpose it serves by being in the river. Should the dam be built? Why, or why not? Would it make a difference to your answer if the small fish were a good food fish or could be used in some other commercial way, or does its possible extinction constitute a sufficient reason to not build the dam? Explain your answer in detail.

Chapter Summary

I. Key terms
  A. *Speciesism* is a prejudice for one's own species and against other species.
  B. *Sentientism* is the theory that only those beings with mental states should be the subject of moral concern.
  C. *Wholism* is a conception of nature that sees humans and nature together as forming a moral community.
  D. *Vegetarianism* is the refusal to eat the flesh of animals in favor of a diet of vegetables.
  E. An *endangered species* is a species of animals in danger of becoming extinct because of the encroachment of civilization upon the natural environment and because of careless exploitation by human beings.

II. Nature and morality
  A. Human beings have discovered in recent years that natural resources, including animals, plants, and trees, are not boundless but are subject to diminishment, destruction, and loss.
  B. This will affect us with regard to the social aspect of our morality, but many consider that nature also is valuable in itself.

III. Environmental ethical issues
  A. We cannot continue the waste and destruction of natural resources, but must take action now to conserve and replenish what we take from nature for our own uses.
  B. Neither can we continue to exploit, misuse, and pollute the environment.
  C. There also is the ethical issue of animal rights.
    1. Many people feel that with our modern products and food availability, we no longer should be destroying animals for food and body parts (fur, skin, tusks).
    2. Also, we must be much more humane in the way we raise domestic animals for food.
    3. We either should not use animals at all for scientific experimentation or use them only sparingly and, again, humanely.
    4. We must also be more careful to ensure that various animal species are not decimated or made extinct.

IV. Our attitude toward nature and what lies behind it
  A. These attitudes have not developed overnight.

  B. Platonic dualism and the beginnings of Western philosophy, which essentially saw human beings as being separate from and superior to the external world and nature, tended to split human beings off from nature.
  C. Judeo-Christian teachings in the Bible taught that human beings are imbued with a soul whereas the rest of nature is not, and that human beings have dominion over all of nature and should "go forth and multiply."
  D. With the advancement of science and technology nature has become, at least from the human point of view, more and more subservient to human beings.
  E. Industrialization not only has increased the use of natural resources for its operation but also has polluted the environment through the disposing of waste.
  F. Through industrialization, population increases, and the greater need for land and space, civilization has encroached upon nature, destroying more and more of the natural environment.

V. Arguments for use and exploitation of the natural environment
  A. There are two types of the dominion-over-nature argument.
    1. Religious: Western religions seem to condone this type of dominion citing various statements in the Bible.
    2. Natural order and evolution: In this view, human beings are considered to be the highest evolved species in nature, so they should exercise power over the rest of it.
  B. Civilization is more important than nature. Because humans constitute the highest evolutionary and religious order, human civilization should take precedence over nature.
  C. Humans and only humans are deserving of moral rights and obligations.

VI. Arguments against the use and exploitation of nature
  A. Monistic wholism versus dominion and domination. Human beings and nature are parts of a whole and not separated into dominant and subordinate groups.
    1. Religious arguments about the superiority of humans have either been misinterpreted or are irrelevant.

2. That humans have evolved to a higher level of intelligence does not mean they automatically are entitled to dominion over nature. Someday they could be replaced by a more advanced species.

3. The proper relationship between human beings and nature is wholistic rather than dominant and subordinate.

B. Reasoning should not separate humans from nature but should unite them both more closely. Reasoning should lead to an acceptance of nature as being intrinsically valuable.

C. Nature, which contains most human needs and which relates to humans in a vital way, should never be made subordinate to civilization, which is human constructed.

VII. The moderate position

A. Nature is important and significant but not necessarily on the same footing with humans.

B. It may therefore be used for human ends but with care so as not to endanger or destroy it.

C. This position generally agrees with the wholistic position but is not against using nature for the good of humans as long as it is done carefully, allowing for the preservation and protection of the environment.

VIII. Criteria for animal rights

A. One criterion states that anything that is alive is deserving of moral consideration. Critics would argue against this.

1. It is too vague and unrealistic, and also it seems to violate the way in which nature itself works (e.g., the natural food chain).

2. Even human life is not valued merely for its own sake; the taking of human life can be declared to be moral under certain circumstances.

B. Those who have interests have rights. Therefore, because animals have interests (e.g., to survive, not to suffer pain), they have rights.

C. Attributes of soul, mind, and feelings. Some would argue that moral consideration is based upon whether or not beings have these attributes.

1. The difficulty of proving the existence of a soul is a problem with this argument as is the question of why such an attribute should be the only criterion for moral consideration. And who knows whether or not animals have souls? Some religions believe they do.

2. Animals have both minds and feelings and therefore satisfy this aspect of the criterion.

D. Proponents would state that animals seem to possess the power of reason, at least at the rudimentary level (e.g., chimpanzees and gorillas can learn sign language) and therefore should be considered as having moral rights.

1. Some humans have severe mental impairment and can barely reason, if at all. If we have moral obligations toward them, why not toward animals?

2. It would seem that a creature's having mental states at all (being sentient) would require from us at least the obligation not to inflict pain upon it.

3. Opponents of animal rights would argue that any mental states that animals may have are so far below those of humans that animals are deserving of little or no moral concern.

IX. Ways of dealing with animal rights

A. True vegetarians (vegans) do not use animals for food at all.

B. There are arguments against vegetarianism.

1. Even if animals have rights, they are less important than the rights of humans, so the latter have a right to use the former for food, just as animals use other animals, according to nature's way.

2. Sentientism, which states that animals should be morally respected because they have mental states, is criticized because it tends to eliminate nonanimal life-forms such as plants, flowers, and trees.

3. Advocates of wholism would argue that sentientism and vegetarianism are too narrow and merely single out one aspect of nature for moral concern; they argue that all of nature is deserving of such respect. Critics of wholism, on the other hand, argue that it blurs proper distinctions in the hierarchy of beings in nature.

X. Use of animals for food

A. Is it moral to kill sentient beings possessing all of the attributes previously described, and use them for food?

B. Ways of raising animals for food.

1. In the past, domesticated animals were raised in the open air on ranches or farms.

2. Now, given the greater demand for meat and other animal products (e.g., eggs,

milk), factory farming, in which animals often are raised in narrow pens without light and air and often are separated from their mothers, is the method used.

C. The vegetarian is absolutely against raising animals for food; moreover, vegetarians are aghast at the current methods used.

D. The carnivore (meat eater) feels that the main purpose of raising animals is for food and that any method that will give human beings better-quality meat more efficiently is certainly acceptable.

E. The moderate position condones using animals for food but does not accept wholesale slaughter, factory farming, or mistreatment of any kind where animals are concerned.

XI. Use of animals for experimentation

A. There are several arguments for animal experimentation.

1. Scientists argue that without our ability to use animals for experimentation, humans would have to be used and would be harmed or killed, or no cures for diseases could ever be found.

2. Because, by law, humans cannot be used for experimentation without their informed consent and the application of strict guidelines, scientific and medical progress would simply come to a standstill without animals.

3. They argue further that animals have much less value than human beings, so it is morally correct to use the former for purposes of experimentation.

4. Many of the animals used would just be put to sleep anyway because they are not wanted; therefore, why not have their deaths serve a purpose and help human beings?

B. Arguments against using animals for experimentation also exist.

1. Animals are thinking and feeling beings that suffer pain to the same extent and degree as do humans; therefore, it is immoral to make animals suffer and die merely so that humans can make progress in science and medicine.

2. Furthermore, many experiments are absolutely unnecessary to the health and well-being of human beings and are done simply out of scientific curiosity.

3. Animal rights activists feel that it is absolutely immoral to use animals for any experiments and that if other means cannot be found, then scientific progress simply will not be able to be made.

C. There is also a moderate position.

1. Moderates would not be opposed to using animals for experimentation but would insist that such experiments must be absolutely necessary to the health and well-being of humans and not be done merely in order to satisfy human curiosity.

2. Care must be taken not to inflict upon animals more pain and suffering during the experiment than is absolutely necessary—every effort must be made to keep animals out of pain while experiments are going on.

XII. Killing animals for sport

A. There are arguments for killing animals for sport.

1. Hunting is an ancient activity that is a significant rite of manhood. It was done in the earliest tribes and cultures and should continue on even today.

2. It is the best way of keeping the animal population under control; if not controlled, animals will destroy our crops, kill our domesticated animals, and encroach upon our cities.

3. There is a need for wild animal meat and body parts.

(a) Even though they have all the domesticated animal meat they might need, many people prefer wild game, such as venison and pheasant, and they should be allowed to indulge their tastes.

(b) Even though clothes and other items can be made from the skins of domestic animals or from synthetic products, the more exotic skins and body parts (snake skin, elephant tusks, fur) are prettier and rarer, and so valued more highly.

(c) It is exciting to have the heads of wild animals a hunter has killed displayed on the walls, and it is unique to have such possessions as elephant-foot wastebaskets.

B. There are also arguments against killing animals for sport.

1. Hunting is an ancient activity that is, however, no longer required. Men originally hunted in order to gain for food and clothing,

but now both can be acquired without killing wild animals in order to do so.

    2. The animal population will control itself if humans will only allow it to do so. Killing animals such as the mountain lion has eliminated from nature predators that would control other animal populations by hunting and killing them for food.

    3. There is absolutely no further need for wild game or body parts, given the plethora of domesticated animal meat and wonderful human-made products, such as synthetic furs, that are now available.

  C. The moderate position seeks a midpoint between the extremes.

    1. Killing for sport can be allowed on a limited basis as long as endangered species are protected and other species don't become endangered.

    2. There is no reason to kill wild animals for meat or body parts except where and when it is allowed within the limits of (1) previously mentioned.

XIII. Protection of endangered species

  A. An irreverence for even a small segment of life affects one's reverence for all life.

  B. Most species are beautiful or at least interesting and different, and they should be available not only for us but also our children, grandchildren, and great-grandchildren to see.

  C. All animals seem to contribute in some way to the balance of nature and its food chain,

and we should be careful not to upset that balance.

XIV. Non-Western perspectives on environmental issues

  A. Because environmental problems are global in scope and implications raised by these important issues of concern affect people the world over, it will be worthwhile to briefly note the value of non-Western ethical viewpoints.

  B. The immanent worldviews of Hinduism and Buddhism, which stress the oneness and interconnectedness of the natural order, present clear alternatives to Western transcendent perspectives where human beings stand over/against nature.

  C. The grand goal of Chinese thought is to achieve harmony and balance.

  D. In Daoist thought the key concept is the *dao*—the way. It refers to the way of ultimate reality, the way of nature, and, ethically, the way that one ought to live.

  E. Confucianism attempts to extend the way by establishing social conventions and Kongzi ritualized proper conduct in order that life, in effect, becomes a performance that is designed to further natural harmony.

  F. In a world of pluralistic cultural values an expanded field of possibilities makes room for alternative responses to serious environmental challenges that are not easily resolved within the limitations of a single cultural viewpoint.

✓●—**Study** and **Review** on **mythinkinglab.com**

Exercises for Review

1. What do the following key terms mean, and how do they relate to environmental ethics: *speciesism, sentientism, wholism, vegetarianism,* and *endangered species?*

2. Do you agree with the view that we have come to our destructive attitudes concerning the environment from our backgrounds in Western philosophy and Western religion? Why or why not? If you do not believe that either has had anything to do with these attitudes, then what has caused us to have them? Answer in detail.

3. If you believe that the Judeo-Christian Bible really does not condone the way in which we control, waste, and destroy nature, then present evidence from the Bible or

Judeo-Christian teachings that encourage reverence, protection, and preservation of nature.

4. Do you think the only and major reason for preserving and protecting nature is to protect our own good, or do you feel that we have a moral obligation toward nature because it is intrinsically valuable? Present arguments in detail.

5. Present arguments as to why we should protect endangered species. What differences does it really make if certain species become extinct? Doesn't nature itself cause some species to become extinct? What difference does it make if human beings do the same thing? Answer in detail.

6. Which is more important: civilization and progress or the natural environment? Why?

7. Do you believe that animals have rights, and do you believe that we have an obligation to see that these rights are protected? Why or why not? If you argue that they do have rights, what are they, and why?

8. What is your position on vegetarianism, and why? Defend or attack the vegetarian position, giving good reasons and arguments for whichever side you take.

9. Do you believe we should use animals for experimentation purposes? Why, or why not? Take a pro, con, or moderate position, and say why you have chosen it.

10. Do you think it is moral to hunt animals for meat, body parts, or sport? Why, or why not? Give good reasons for your answer.

11. Select an important issue in environmental ethics and analyze it from a Hindu, Buddhist, Daoist, or Confucian perspective.

Views of the Major Ethical Theories on Environmental Ethics

Describe as fully as you can how each of the major ethical theories—Ethical Egoism, Utilitarianism, Divine Command Theory, Kant's Duty Ethics, Ross's *Prima Facie* Duties, and Virtue Ethics—probably would deal with the ethical issues related to the environment including the cases at the end of the chapter.

Ethics Problem[10]
How Can We Understand an Obligation to the Environment?

When taking up the matter of environmental ethics, many people affirm that we have a moral obligation to protect the environment. I don't want to ask if you agree or disagree, but rather if you can make sense of the claim at all. Can we have an obligation to the environment itself, or are we really saying that we have obligations to people (present or future who rely upon the environment)? If we can have a direct obligation to the environment, what is it about an environment that is the proper recipient of that obligation? Is it the animal life in it? Is it the land itself? Do we have the same obligations to all environments (desert and rain forest alike)?

If our obligation is really to the people who depend upon the environment, would we be doing anything *intrinsically wrong* if we destroyed our planet? That is, imagine we developed adequate space travel such that we could find and colonize another suitable planet for all to live on. If every person was safe, prosperous, and consenting on the new planet, would we be doing anything inherently wrong by wringing the last resource out of this planet until every ecosystem was literally destroyed?

Notes

1. Joel Feinberg, "The Rights of Animals and Unborn Generations," in *Philosophical Environmental Crisis,* ed. W. Blackstone (Athens, GA: University of Georgia Press, 1974), 48–68.

2. James White, ed., *Contemporary Moral Problems,* 2nd edn. (St. Paul, MN: West, 1988), 315.

3. Ibid.

4. Michael C. Brannigan, *The Pulse of Wisdom: The Philosophies of India, China and Japan,* 2nd edn. (Belmont, CA: Wadsworth/Thompson Learning, 2000), 4.

5. Ward J. Fellows, *Religions East and West* (New York: Holt, Rinehart and Winston, 1979), 71.

6. Saral Jhingran, *Aspects of Hindu Morality* (Delhi: Motilal Banarsidass, 1989), 34.

7. James Legge, trans., *The Tao Te Ching of Lao Tzu* (New York: Dover Publications, Inc., 1962), 25.

8. Roger T. Ames and Henry Rosemont Jr., trans., *The Analects of Confucius: A Philosophical Translation* (New York: Ballantine, 1998), 74.

9. Ann Landers, "For Fur or Food, Killing's the Same," *The Bakersfield Californian* 103, no. 86 (March 27, 1989), D4.

10. Ethics Problem, "How Can We Understand an Obligation to the Environment?" was written by John Santiago and used with his permission.

Read the **Document** on **mythinkinglab.com**

"Challenges in Environmental Ethics," Holmes Rolston III,
"The Case for Animal Rights," Tom Regan.

Who Could Object to Wind Power?

Margaret Wente

Margaret Wente is one of Canada's leading columnists. As a writer for The Globe and Mail, *she provokes heated debate with her views on health care, education, and social issues. She is this year's winner of the National Newspaper Award for column writing. She has edited* Canadian Business *and* ROB Magazine. *She has also been editor of the* Globe's *business section and the ROB, and managing editor of the paper. Her columns have appeared in the* Globe *since 1992. For the past two years she has been writing full-time for the paper, and she is a frequent commentator on television and radio. This article originally appeared in* The Globe and Mail *on November 25, 2008.*

1　On Toronto's waterfront stands a mighty wind turbine, its blades rotating lazily in the breeze (at least sometimes). It's a monument to good intentions and civic virtue. The Mayor loves it. The Premier loves it. All governments love wind power, because it makes them look so green. David Suzuki, the patron saint of environmentalism, compares wind turbines to medieval cathedrals—the highest expressions of human achievement. Wind is clean, sustainable, renewable, free. Who could possibly object?

The citizens. Last night in Toronto, hundreds of anxious folks jammed a meeting called to discuss plans for a massive wind farm along the shore of Lake Ontario. They fear the 90-metre turbines will chop up birds, disrupt migration routes, destroy views, lower property values, even make them sick.

NIMBYs? No doubt. But they have a lot of company. Across Canada, Britain and Europe, a growing protest movement is arguing that wind farms are no good for the environment.

Here's another reason not to like them. Wind power can't survive without massive subsidies, courtesy of you and me. "If these hidden subsidies were taken away, there would not be a single wind turbine built in Britain," says David Bellamy, a well-known environmentalist who has been tramping the Scottish countryside to oppose a massive wind project there.

5   Subsidies might be okay if wind could help replace conventional energy one day. It can't. "If the whole of Wales was covered with wind turbines, the nation would generate only a sixth of the U.K.'s energy needs," says Prof. David MacKay, a physicist at Cambridge. He's all in favour of clean, renewable energy. But he's done the math.

The biggest problem with wind is that it doesn't always blow. There are lots of days when Toronto's monument to civic virtue couldn't even power my toaster. Inconveniently, these times of low production tend to coincide with times of high demand. So no matter how many turbines you put up, you always need backup power. Usually that means fossil fuel, or, in Ontario's case, nuclear.

The biggest advertisements for wind power are Germany and Denmark. Germany has more wind turbines than any other country in the world, and Chancellor Angela Merkel has draped herself in green. But wind energy can't replace conventional power there either, so Germany is also building dozens of new coal-fired power plants. Denmark, with the largest offshore wind farm in the world, brags that 20 per cent of the electricity it generates comes from wind. But more than half its wind power is exported, because that's the only way the system can work.

Here at home, wind companies have been scrambling to get their share of $1.5-billion in federal subsidies for clean energy. On top of that, they get a premium when they sell the power. Ontario pays them 11 to 14 cents per kilowatt hour. Conventional energy goes for about half that price.

"Ontario is turning to wind turbines to help create jobs and power a green energy future," brags a government press release. But wind companies are chasing another green. The biggest wind project in the world, on the Thames Estuary, nearly collapsed last spring when a major backer, Shell, pulled out. Shell said the "incentives" were better in the United States.

10   Fortunately, a lot of wind companies won't survive the recession. One big Canadian firm, EarthFirst, is under court protection. Wind companies need a huge amount of credit, which has dried up. Expen-

sive wind power makes a lot less sense with oil back around $50. And the global slump will do more to cut greenhouse gas emissions than all the wind turbines and solar panels David Suzuki can dream of.

When will we stop pouring billions into wind? I have no idea. Politicians really love their turbines. Meantime, that soft whooshing sound you hear is your friendly green government, vacuuming money out of your pockets.

Structure and Content

1. What does the second sentence of this article tell us about the author's point of view? Is this tone continued throughout the introductory paragraph? Explain your answer with specific reference to the text.
2. What are the advantages to wind power? What are the disadvantages?
3. What kinds of evidence does Wente use to support her points? Do you find it convincing? Why or why not?

Further Discussion

1. One of Wente's arguments against wind power is that it is expensive, especially compared to more traditional sources of energy, such as fossil fuels. Is the cost a good enough reason to abandon the technology? Why or why not?
2. Would you be willing to pay more for your energy costs if you knew that the energy came from environmentally responsible sources? Why or why not? Do you think your answer would change if you ran your own business?

Suggestions for Writing

1. Should governments use taxpayer money to fund green power initiatives? Why or why not?
2. Research wind power, clean coal technology, and other "green" sources of energy. According to what you have learned, can they ever be good for both the environment and business?

Bioethics—Ethical Issues in Medicine

((●─[**Listen** to the **Chapter Audio** on **mythinkinglab.com**

This chapter, which is concerned with bioethics, is here in order to show how ethics is applied in specific aspects of society and human life and how ethical problems and issues affect human beings at all levels and in all areas of life. As a matter of fact, ethical problems arising in areas such as medicine and business have fostered a revival of interest in ethics, not only as theory or as an aspect of religion but also as something that must be applied to human affairs in a practical way. The issues that have arisen in medicine have served as the greatest catalyst in our time for the renewed interest in applied ethics.

OBJECTIVES

After you have read this chapter, you should be able to

1. Know how ethics can be applied to specific areas of human life, such as bioethics.
2. Know what the term *bioethics* means, and describe the areas and issues it covers.
3. Understand the rights and obligations of health care professionals and patients and their families as they are defined according to three different views: paternalism, radical individualism, and reciprocity.
4. Understand the importance of truth telling, confidentiality, and informed consent to significant relationships between professionals and patients.
5. Understand what some of the ethical issues are in the areas of allocation of scarce medical resources, behavior control, human experimentation, and genetics.

WHAT IS BIOETHICS?

Bioethics means "life ethics," or ethics in medicine. It covers a larger area of concern than the phrase "medical ethics," which often is used to refer strictly to the doctor–patient relationship or to such issues as whether doctors should advertise, split fees, or report incompetence within their ranks. Bioethics covers the following areas in medicine: treatment of dying patients, allowing someone to die, mercy death, and mercy killing; behavior control; human experimentation and informed consent; genetics, fertilization, and birth; health care delivery and its costs; population and birth control, abortion, and sterilization; allotment of scarce medical resources, organ transplantation, and hemodialysis; stem cell research and cloning; and truth telling and confidentiality in medicine.

In short, what bioethics really is concerned with is the establishment and maintenance of vital and moral human relationships between the sick and the dying on the one hand and the healthy and medical professionals on the other. It is concerned with "treatment" in the broadest sense; that is, it deals not only with how we treat patients in a medical sense but also with how we relate to, or deal with, our fellow human beings, especially in matters of illness, injury, dying, and death.

HEALTH CARE PROFESSIONALS AND PATIENTS AND THEIR FAMILIES—RIGHTS AND OBLIGATIONS

Health care professionals are doctors, nurses, attendants or aides, therapists, technicians, and all others involved in medical aid. There are three major views of what the relationship between health care professionals and patients and their families should be.

Paternalism

Paternalism, as the name suggests, is the position that argues that health care professionals should take a parental role toward patients and their families. According to this position, professionals have a superior knowledge of medicine; therefore, they and they alone are privileged, because of their long and specialized training, to decide what is in the best interest of patients and their families. This attitude is characterized by the old cliché "The doctor always knows best."

A number of arguments are put forth to support this viewpoint. First of all, laypeople lack the professional knowledge of medicine to deal with both physical and mental illness and injury; therefore, they have no way of knowing what is best for them. Second, because of their long, hard professional education and because of their experience, professionals (especially doctors) know the characteristics of diseases and injuries; therefore, patients should place themselves totally in the professionals' hands. Finally, any and all decisions about patients' care and treatment, including the information that should be given to them and decisions concerning hospitalization, tests, and so on, should be completely in the hands of the doctors and their professional assistants. Patients must trust them and not interfere with the treatment suggested.

Under paternalism, there are two possible models: the engineering model and the priestly model.

THE ENGINEERING MODEL. According to Robert Veatch, a renowned bioethicist, this model is an outgrowth of the biological revolution in which a physician behaves like an applied scientist. As such a scientist, the physician must be value free and purely scientific in his approach to treating patients. Physicians in this model, therefore, supposedly separate themselves from any values that they or their patients might have. These physicians are "engineers," technically and mechanically well qualified to treat their patients as if the latter were biological machines.

The foolishness and dangers of this model have been powerfully revealed in the development of the atomic and hydrogen bombs and in Nazi medical research and experimentation on human beings in World War II. Also, such physicians cannot logically be value free because each choice and decision they make requires a frame of values on which they are based. Practically every decision physicians make on a daily basis requires them to consider values. For example, whether to give a genuine drug or a placebo or whether to start or stop treatment of a patient is as much a value as a medical decision. Further, if physicians could really be value free, that would make them mere engineers or plumbers, making repairs, connecting tubes, and flushing out systems with no questions asked.[1]

PRIESTLY MODEL. The second model that Veatch describes goes to the opposite extreme, making the physician a new priest. Veatch quotes Robert Wilson, a sociologist of medicine, as saying, "The doctor's office or the hospital . . . have somewhat the aura of a sanctuary. . . ."[2] Therefore, physicians now are acting as priests toward their patients who are their "parishioners," and the emphasis is placed on the ethical principle of "benefit and do no harm to the patient." This certainly is not an insignificant principle, but according to Veatch, there are other principles that may be overlooked because of an emphasis on this one principle, such as protecting individual freedom, preserving individual dignity, truth telling and promise keeping, and maintaining and restoring justice. By emphasizing the first principle described, the other principles may be ignored. The other problem with this theory is that the physician as priest is still making the decisions for the patient and doing, as priest, what he thinks "is best for the patient."[3]

Radical Individualism

Radical individualism is the position that patients have absolute rights over their own bodies and lives and therefore may reject all the recommendations of health care personnel (especially doctors).

There are a number of arguments supporting this position. First, doctors are human like everyone else, and they are capable of making errors in judgment, diagnosis, prognosis, and treatment. They are even at times guilty of malpractice, negligence, or maltreatment. Second, patients (or their families when patients are totally incapacitated) are best qualified to decide if, how, when, and what treatment is to be given; after all, their bodies and lives are at stake, not those of the professionals. Third, many issues having to do with treatment are not strictly medical, and professionals sometimes are not qualified to make appropriate decisions concerning such issues (e.g., at what point debilitating, painful treatment should be stopped, because its negative effects outweigh any curative powers it may have). Fourth, with the expansion of media information, such as the Internet, these days laypeople are better educated about their bodies and minds and about the illnesses and injuries that affect them. They are also able to understand their medical condition, diagnoses, and prognoses if professionals will only have the kindness and courtesy to explain things to them clearly and in plain language. Because they can understand these things, they are qualified to make decisions about how they should or should not be treated. Finally, paternalism has often led to total patient dependence and sometimes to complete dehumanization, with a patient being regarded merely as a living body to be investigated, analyzed, medicated, or operated on without recognition that a *person* still resides within it.

The problem with this view is that it places *all* decisions in the hands of patients, who may not be as knowledgeable about their medical problems or as well qualified to make such crucial decisions as they need to be. Second, many patients do not want to be responsible for making decisions completely on their own without the help of their families or health care personnel, including their doctors.

The Reciprocal View

The reciprocal view involves a team approach to treatment much like that described in the hospice approach to care for the dying. In this view, patients and their families are key members of the team, and doctors, nurses, and other health care professionals work together to do what's best for patients and their families. This position is supported by a number of arguments, some of which are similar to those made for radical individualism.

First, professionals, particularly doctors, are neither gods nor valid father figures; rather, they are human beings with specialized education, training, and experience, which makes them an important element in the care of patients and their families.

Second, many of the decisions concerning the treatment of patients and their families are not strictly medical in nature and therefore should not be made solely by medical professionals. Doctors need to rely on other health care personnel, such as nurses; psychiatric, physical, and occupational therapists; and nurses' aides. They also need the support of non-medical personnel such as clergy, social workers, and trained volunteers if they are to properly treat patients and their families as whole human beings rather than medical specimens.

Third, it is important to recognize the right of individual patients to make free choices concerning their treatment because it is their bodies and lives that are at stake. Although, as already discussed, such a right is not "absolute" but is and should be given high priority. The recognition of this right is exemplified by the creation and dissemination of a list of patients' rights. In addition to the right to participate actively in decisions regarding medical care, including the right to refuse treatment, patients also have the right to considerate and respectful care; information about their diagnosis, treatment, and prognosis; the information they require in order to give their informed consent to any procedure; and full knowledge about human experimentation, and the right to refuse it.[4]

All of this means that neither patients nor professionals alone "know best," but that decisions involving care and treatment are to be reciprocal (i.e., involving give and take) rather than dictatorial, paternalistic, or anarchistic. Obviously, professionals do "know best" in certain areas, but they should share their information and expertise with patients and their families. In this way, proper recommendations can be made as to alternatives of care and treatment, and proper decision making can be accomplished. Furthermore, patients and their families are entitled to more than one professional opinion.

Patients must realize, however, that no matter how well informed they are, they can't know everything about medicine, and they must defer to professionals in some areas. However, once they have become well informed (and they have a right to be), they certainly are qualified to make decisions about their care and treatment. In some areas, they definitely "know best." In other words, patients and their families are entitled to be apprised of all the expertise that can be brought to bear on their cases so that they can make important decisions. According to this view, in short, all decisions should be arrived at through a free exchange of ideas and a full discussion of alternative methods of care and treatment, with final decisions being made jointly by patients or their families (when patients are incapacitated) and their doctors.

In other words, reciprocal care calls for proper, intelligent, and informed communication between patients and their doctors. Doctors can facilitate such communication, as one family practice doctor in Seattle did, by furnishing their patients with a list of questions to ask:

1. What is wrong with me?
2. What caused it?
3. What should be done about it?
4. What will it cost?
5. How long will it take?
6. What tests should be done and why?
7. What is my prognosis?
8. What will you do next?
9. Is it necessary?
10. Is it dangerous?
11. Do I have any alternatives? If so, what are they?
12. If I must go into the hospital, how long will I be there?
13. How long will I be laid up, and when can I go back to school or work?[5]

Such a list of questions can really help to stimulate communication between doctors and patients and also enhance the doctor–patient relationship.

There are two models under the reciprocal view: the collegial model and the contractual model.

THE COLLEGIAL MODEL. In this model, " . . . the physician and the patient should see themselves as colleagues pursuing a common goal of eliminating the illness and preserving the health of the patient. The physician is the patient's 'pal.'"[6]

Veatch sees the problem here as being that of whether doctors and patients can really assume mutual loyalty and goals of common interest. He goes on to say that ethnic, class, economic, and value differences make the collegial model more of an ideal than a reality.[7]

THE CONTRACTUAL MODEL. Veatch goes on to say that what is needed is " . . . a more provisional model which permits equality in the realm of moral significance between patient and physician without making the utopian assumption of collegiality."[8] This contract should not be merely legalistic but more like a covenant as in the traditional religious or marriage sense. The bases for such a contract are freedom, dignity, truth telling, promise keeping, and justice, and there must be trust and confidence even though there is not a full mutuality of interests because of the value differences described previously.

Veatch believes that "Only in the contractual model can there be a true sharing of ethical authority and responsibility . . . " because this model " . . . avoids the moral abdication on the part of the physician in the engineering model and the moral abdication on the part of the patient in the priestly model. It also avoids the uncontrolled and false sense of equality in the collegial model."[9]

The difficulties associated with this model are how to execute the contract (oral or written) and what to include in it. Isn't this all rather vague? The health care field already has several contractual type forms—advance directives and various "Do Not Resuscitate" forms that the patient may sign—but Veatch seems to be talking about an agreement that is something more than these kinds of forms: an overall contract for medical care.

At any rate, it is important in using this model (1) to know the patients and to base the contractual relationship on their needs and personalities; (2) when in doubt, to err on the side of patient autonomy; and (3) to be cognizant of how power asymmetries and the fact of illness affect interactions and communication between physician and patient.

TRUTH TELLING AND INFORMED CONSENT

The issue involving truth telling is to what extent patients and their families should be told the truth about their illnesses, injuries, and/or dying. The term *informed consent* refers to a formalized procedure whereby patients (or family members, when patients are incapacitated) "consent," usually in writing, to some sort of medical treatment, procedure, or surgery that may have questionable side effects, affect patients' future lives, or even involve the risk of death. Somewhat akin to the discussion of patients' and professionals' rights and obligations, there are two views of truth telling in medicine: the paternalistic view and that of the patients' right to know.

The Paternalistic View of Truth Telling

There are several arguments put forth to support the paternalistic viewpoint. First, because patients are not medically trained, they cannot understand what doctors tell them; therefore, they do not need to know more than the fact that professionals are doing their very best for them. Second, it is best both for patients' morale and for their will to get better or will to live if they are not told the truth—especially if it is bad news, because full knowledge of their situation might cause them to "lose heart" and not fight to survive. Third, it would serve no purpose to give them bad news, because if the prognosis is that they are going to die, for example, they will die anyway; therefore, one should let them live out the time they have left as happily as they can. Fourth, it is all right to tell the families but not the patients—patients should be protected from bad news. Finally, it is important for the doctor, nurses, and other professionals, as well as the family members, to avoid "being morbid" by discussing with patients the seriousness of their illnesses, injuries, or dying. Everyone connected with patients should try to cheer them up and to deny bad news whenever possible.

The Patients' Right to Know

There are a number of arguments made in support of the patients' right to know, many of them criticisms of the paternalistic arguments. First, because it is the patients' bodies and lives that are involved, not those of the health care professionals or even other family members, patients have a right to know everything and should be told all. Second, it is much easier to treat and deal with patients if they are aware of what is going on and if professionals and family members don't have to constantly pretend that patients' illnesses or injuries are not serious or that patients are not dying.[10] Third, patients often become angry when they don't know in advance about the side effects or other painful or disturbing aspects of treatment. (E.g., a woman whose radiation therapy made her arm swell and become very painful became angry because she was never told she might have this problem.)

One negative aspect of the patients' rights position is that some professionals adopt this view so fervently that they are brutally frank with their patients, often leaving them without any hope or frightening them unnecessarily. It is a false dilemma to assume that you either must give people terrible news or lie to them.

The Moderate Position

A third view, one that lies somewhere between paternalism and brutal frankness, is a sharing of appropriate information with patients when they do want to know it and to the extent that they want to know it. This view lets patients be the guide in determining the information they will receive. It involves the following aspects:

1. Listening to patients carefully and hearing what they are really asking or trying to ask.
2. Not avoiding persistent, roundabout, or direct questions, but rather answering them truthfully yet not brutally.
3. Not forcing information on patients when they are not ready just because the professional is ready to discuss the matter or is too busy to wait until patients are ready.
4. Not avoiding the truth by using medical and technical language or jargon, but trying instead to explain in lay terms everything that patients need or want to know.
5. Being aware that explanations or answers may have to be given in gradual doses or more than once because human beings will often defend themselves against the shock of bad news by not really "hearing" what is being said.
6. Always telling the truth clearly, gently, and humanely, never brutally, coldly, hopelessly, or cruelly.
7. Never leaving patients and their families without some hope, even if it is only the hope that professionals will keep trying to do the very best they can to cure patients and to keep them comfortable and out of pain.

Informed Consent

As mentioned earlier, *informed consent* is a more formalized approach to truth telling and to involving patients in decisions concerning their treatment. This approach has become necessary in our time because of the many complex technological tests, procedures, and surgeries required not only for individual therapeutic reasons but also for experiments that can help science to benefit others (by testing reactions to new drugs, for example). The problems of human experimentation will be discussed later in this chapter.

In our country, the Department of Health and Welfare, with the agreement of the American Medical Association (AMA) and most hospitals, mandates that patients on whom complex, painful, risky, or dangerous procedures need to be performed, either for their own good or for the good of others, should be fully "informed" of what is to be done, why it is to be done, when it is to be done, and what to expect in the way of pain, discomfort, or risk. For example, except in emergency situations—in which saving a life requires immediate action—patients or their closest next of kin (wife, husband, parents, and children) must authorize any procedure of a serious nature such as surgeries and laboratory tests of certain kinds, as well as certain types of therapy, such as chemotherapy or radiation therapy.

The assumption behind the "informed consent" approach is that in order to intelligently "consent" to a procedure, patients must be fully "informed"; furthermore, they must agree in writing to undergo the procedure in order to avoid any later confusions and legal complications that may arise from it. In order to facilitate the informed consent procedure, many hospitals and laboratory groups have printed informed consent forms for patients to read and sign. These forms should do the following: Explain the procedure and its purpose clearly and in ordinary language; explain what kinds of discomfort or pain the procedure may cause patients to feel before, during, and after its completion; explain any and all complications that may arise because of the procedure; state how long the procedure will take; include a statement that the patient's doctors have judged that the procedure should be performed, for the patient's best interests and welfare and despite any discomforts or risks. Figure 14-1 provides an example of an informed consent document.

Four factors may inhibit informed consent (1) the nature of illness of or injury to patients and the various medications they may be taking; (2) physicians' attitudes; for example, arrogance; (3) patients' attitudes; for example, submissiveness; and (4) power asymmetries.

The best approach to getting informed consent is for the physician who is requiring or performing the procedure to explain it in some detail in addition to having the patient read the form. Patients and their families also should be encouraged to ask any questions they wish and should be given honest and clear answers. The idea behind such verbal explanations is that when patients sign these forms, it is important that they have truly been fully informed; merely reading a paper is often not enough, especially when patients are confused, worried, or even scared about the procedure.

Doctors' Reactions to Truth Telling and Informed Consent

Some doctors are opposed to full disclosure of truth to their patients and are also opposed to informed consent, except as a mere formality. First of all, such doctors feel that patients don't need to be fully informed because doctors know what they are doing and explanations of complicated medical procedures will only confuse patients and break down the relationship of faith and trust that should exist between doctor and patient (engineering or priestly paternalism).

Permit for Percutaneous Trans-Hepatic Cholangiography

The term *percutaneous trans-hepatic cholangiography* means a study of the bile ducts (part of the drainage system of the liver) that is performed by entering a bile duct in the liver with a catheter (tube) that is passed through the skin to reach the proper position. Your doctor has requested that we perform a trans-hepatic cholangiogram on you to help him in his care of you. Because this type of examination is probably new to you, this note is intended to explain what you should expect.

Trans-hepatic cholangiography is performed by introducing a small catheter into a bile duct in the liver. The catheter is introduced in combination with a sharp stylet (special needle). It will be passed through the skin under your right ribs. More than one attempt may be needed to position the catheter. It is unusual to make more than four complete attempts. Once the catheter is positioned, an "x-ray dye" will be injected and films will be taken in several projections to help to identify your problem.

What will you feel? You will be sedated before the procedure, and, if needed, more sedation can be given during the procedure. We will use a local anesthetic where the catheter is introduced. This will sting and burn for about 30 to 40 seconds. Insertion of the catheter is done with a rapid motion and often causes a sharp pain, which is generally short-lived. The major source of discomfort is leakage of bile or blood around the catheter into the abdomen. This is painful but can be treated with pain medication. This leakage is unpredictable, but probably occurs in 10 to 20% of patients.

What are the complications? The two most common complications have already been mentioned—bile leak and bleeding. Bleeding always occurs but is generally minor. Bile leakage into the abdomen often occurs when a dilated bile duct is entered and may be painful. This problem is the reason why the examination is performed only when surgery is planned to follow. There are a series of other complications related to catheter positioning that are unusual, but we will discuss them with you if you wish. The "x-ray dye" occasionally causes an "allergic" type reaction that cannot be predicted in advance. This generally consists of hives or nausea, but rarely is the reaction life-threatening or fatal (less than 0.0025% or 2 in 100,000 cases). This type of reaction is carefully watched for, and treatment can be instituted promptly should this occur. Occasionally infection of bile ducts can be spread into other parts of the body during the procedure.

The study will take 30 to 60 minutes. We should point out that a negative study—failure to enter a bile duct—provides important clinical information and may be the anticipated result of the study. If this occurs you may be returned to your room.

It is the judgment of your doctor that the potential benefits of this procedure as far as diagnosis of your condition far outweigh any of the above possible complications.

I have read and understand the above statements and have discussed them to my satisfaction and I consent to the performance of the above procedure by a qualified physician assigned by the above medical corporation upon

_____ (Name) _____ (Unit No.) _____ (Date)

_____ (Signature) _____ (Witness)

FIGURE 1 An informed consent document.

Second, patients often don't want to hear explanations, and forcing them to against their wills constitutes an invasion of their rights; furthermore, making them face facts about their physical or mental status or well-being that they aren't ready to accept is a highly questionable, perhaps even dangerous, course of action.

Third, every procedure has its risks, but there is no reason to frighten patients unnecessarily when the odds are only, for example, two in one hundred thousand that a particular allergy or side effect will occur.

Fourth, such explanations may unnecessarily frighten patients to the extent that they will refuse to undergo a procedure that may be necessary to their health or well-being.

Finally, doctors sometimes feel that by describing certain side effects, such as headaches, they can induce such problems through the power of suggestion; that is, patients may worry so much about getting a headache that the worry actually brings one on. Doctors sometimes feel that if patients don't know that they "are supposed to" have some sort of reaction, they won't get it, at least not psychosomatically.

The other extreme in truth telling is, of course, to go overboard and "tell all." Some doctors feel that it is important that patients know every "sordid" detail of what is going to happen to them, whether they want to or not. For example, a woman in her mid-seventies who had broken her hip and was to undergo orthopedic surgery was told by the anesthetist that he was going to use curare, a paralyzing drug, to anesthetize her. He explained in detail how her heart would stop beating for a short while but assured her that he would be able to "bring her back from the dead." The woman told the anesthetist not to give her so many details; to just do his work and not discuss it with her. It would seem that giving information to such an extent really serves no purpose unless the patient insists on knowing *every* last detail, which very few would. Except in such cases, overly detailed explanations merely cause unnecessary anxiety.

Patients' and Families' Reactions to Truth Telling

As we have already mentioned, some doctors base their decisions concerning what information to give on their own judgment as to what patients and their families do or do not want to know. It certainly is true that many patients and families don't want to know the truth; they prefer to deny that "terrible things" are happening to them. However, most patients want to know what is happening to them because it is their bodies and lives that are at risk. Perhaps they don't want or need to know all the details, but they do want to know the crucial facts.

Furthermore, just because patients and their families sometimes want to deny the existence of serious illness, injury, dying, and death doesn't necessarily mean they don't really want to know the truth. After all, there is often "unfinished business" that can be accomplished once the truth has been faced: dealing with inheritance and wills, settling family feuds, resolving other relationship problems, and doing things that families have always wanted to do but have put off. If patients and their families are not told the truth, they can miss an important opportunity to put their lives in order.

A great deal of sensitivity is required on the part of the whole health care team, especially doctors, to know what to tell and when to tell it and to be able to gauge possible reactions of patients and their families to different types of information. The team members must let patients guide them as much as possible in determining what information to give. Needless to say, it is difficult to deal well with the issue of truth telling, and health care professionals—especially doctors—should be given extensive training in patient–professional relationships.

Generally speaking, according to this point of view, patients and their families should be kept as fully informed as possible about their situation, especially when it is clear that they really do want to know. Such openness and honesty help to prevent the often painful game playing that goes on when people aren't honest with each other. Patients and their families should be dealt with truthfully, honestly, and compassionately but without cruelty, coldness, or brutal frankness. If, however, they consistently indicate that they don't want to be told about a specific situation, and if leaving them in ignorance would do no harm to them or their families, then one can avoid telling them until they indicate that they are ready to know. Finally, if patients want to know the truth about their illness but their families don't want them to, the patients' wishes should come first—family members should be counseled to allow the patients to be given the knowledge that they want and need.

CONFIDENTIALITY

Confidentiality in patient–doctor relationships would on the surface seem to be fairly clear—that is, whatever a doctor and patient discuss and whatever the patient reveals in this relationship are to be held in strictest confidence, just as in other professional relationships such as lawyer–client, counselor–client, or rabbi/priest/minister–parishioner relationships. And yet as it turns out, confidentiality is by no means so clear-cut an issue in the doctor–patient relationship. For example, what happens when a doctor tests a patient for a sexually transmitted disease (STD), including AIDS? The law is clear—STDs have to be reported—but it also is clear that test results showing that a patient is HIV positive or has AIDS are generally not to be revealed. Other infectious diseases, such as leprosy, tuberculosis, or plagues, must be reported by individuals' names, but not HIV positive or AIDS results, which can be reported only anonymously as numbers of such cases.

Positive HIV Tests and AIDS

SPOUSES AND PARTNERS.   Because of tremendous misunderstandings concerning the AIDS epidemic and the stigma connected with people who are HIV positive or who have AIDS, laws have protected such people from being singled out because they could lose their jobs, societal status, and even friends if these results were revealed. However, problems have arisen with regard to matters of justice or fairness, especially those relating to sexual partners or drug-using partners. For example, should this information be revealed to such partners or spouses so that they can protect themselves from infection, especially because AIDS is a fatal disease with no cure as of yet?

For example, if a man goes on a trip, has sexual contact with an HIV-positive man or woman, and then tests HIV positive himself, should his wife or other sexual partners be told about his infection, or should his confidentiality be protected as it would be under most other medical circumstances? One solution, of course, is to urge the man to tell his wife or partner or to get his permission to let the physician do so; but what if he refuses?

The Centers for Disease Control (CDC) recommends that if HIV-infected persons are unwilling to notify partners, then physicians should use confidential procedures so as to ensure that partners are notified. Unfortunately, just what is meant by "confidential procedures" is not clear. A California law now permits disclosure by a physician to a spouse or to a needle-sharing partner if attempts to obtain the patient's voluntary consent have failed. The physician, however, is not required to make or not make such disclosure and is protected from liability no matter which approach he or she takes. Both the American Psychological Association (APA) and the American Medical Association (AMA) agree that it is ethically permissible for physicians to notify an identifiable person in danger of contracting the virus from a partner if they have good reason to believe that the infected person has failed to or is unwilling to do so. Another way of resolving this dilemma is to warn infected persons of the limitations of confidentiality before counseling them.

HEALTH CAREGIVERS WITH HIV/AIDS. Another problem has arisen with regard to health caregivers who are HIV positive or who have AIDS. If this information were to be revealed, then most such people would be out of a job; and yet, is it fair to their patients not to know that their health caregivers have this problem? A young woman died as a result of having been infected with the AIDS virus from her dentist, who has also since died from AIDS.

Some health caregivers feel that there would be a double standard if caregivers had to reveal their problems, but patients did not because the livelihoods of the former would be at stake. As health caregivers, they should, of course, take the responsibility for their infectiousness and remove themselves from any part of their work that would involve the possibility of passing on their body fluids to patients. For example, a surgeon should stop doing surgery and retrain or go into a different area within the same medical field for which he or she already is trained. But again, what if such doctors choose not to take that responsibility? What should be done? Shouldn't caregivers have the same protection as anyone else who tests HIV positive or has AIDS?

As one can see, the matter of confidentiality is not always so simple and straightforward as it might at first appear to be. It would seem that, as a general rule, confidentiality should be maintained to the utmost degree. At the same time, however, everything must also be done to protect the innocent from any kind of contagion. In these difficult times, every effort must be put into both of these areas of medicine, and people who are capable of infecting others must bear the responsibility of warning others. If they refuse, then confidential action must be taken so as to protect the innocent. Each case or situation must be dealt with on an individual basis.

GUILT AND INNOCENCE IN TREATING PATIENTS

Another general medical ethical issue that sometimes arises relates to the effect on the treatment of patients by health care professionals, who have judged their patients to be either "guilty" or "innocent"; that is, the degree to which a patient is deemed to be the cause of or contributor to the illness for which he or she is being treated. For example, it often is difficult for a health practitioner to be objective when dealing with alcoholics or drug abusers if any members of his or her family have used alcohol or drugs or, worse yet, died as a result of either form of abuse. Similarly, it must be hard for the parent of a small child to treat a child abuser for an injury or a disease.

This inability to suspend personal feelings that can cloud professional judgment has to some extent always been a problem in medicine, especially when medical personnel are obliged to keep treating patients who continuously abuse themselves and thereby give rise to their own injuries or disease. Allowing personal attitudes to compromise patient care has become a more prevalent dilemma since the increase in the number of AIDS patients. Will a doctor or nurse treat an AIDS patient differently if that patient became infected due to receiving tainted blood from a transfusion as opposed to having acquired the disease as a result of sexual activity or drug abuse? Should this difference in treatment or attitude in giving treatment be allowed for, or not? Perhaps this question can be answered only when we have determined what a health professional's purpose in life is. Most will agree that it is not the job of such a professional to try, judge, or convict any patient of crimes, no matter how heinous. It is, rather, the task of such professionals to treat a sick or injured patient to the best of their knowledge and ability regardless of the patient's religion, race, lifestyle, or alleged or known involvement in criminal activity. Of course, this is often easier said than done, but just as a court reporter must report testimony accurately and without judging the guilt or innocence of a defendant, so must health care professionals treat sick and injured patients as well as they can regardless of those patients' backgrounds. Such professionals need not like these patients or in any way condone what they have done or are doing, but neither must they allow their own preconceptions or feelings to enter into the quality of treatment they give to them.

ETHICAL ISSUES IN MEDICINE

Because this text can serve as no more than an introduction to bioethics, there is only enough space to present problems in three areas: behavior control, human experimentation, and genetics. For a more complete discussion of bioethics, you may want to read some of the texts listed in the "Supplementary Reading" section at the end of this text.

Ethics and Behavior Control

Behavior control is that aspect of bioethics which deals with general questions concerning the extent to which the behavior of human beings should be controlled by the various technologies available to us in our century. In particular, the following specific questions arise:

- How do we determine what constitutes undesirable or socially unacceptable behavior?
- Who defines such behavior, and to what extent should we control or eliminate it?
- Which methods of controlling behavior are considered ethical, and which are not?
- Who should determine how and to whom behavior control is to be applied—the individuals suffering psychological problems, their families, others living around them, the government, their doctors, and medicine in general?

These issues are particularly crucial in cases involving mentally ill patients, prisoners, children, or antisocial human beings.

Before going any further, it is important that we understand precisely what *behavior control* is. It has been defined as the modification, or changing, of individuals' behavior by means of various technologies, with or without their permission and with or without coercion. Some means used in behavior control are drugs, psychotherapy, behavior modification techniques (reward or aversive conditioning), electrical brain stimulation (EBS), hypnotism, biofeedback, surgery, and incarceration.

The major ethical issue that arises in terms of behavior control is that such control involves an encroachment upon or even an elimination of individual freedom: The question, then, is to what extent this should be allowed. Our recent past as well as present history are rife with situations that give rise to these issues. For example, it was discovered that about 200 male sex offenders in California had been given a choice of prison or castration. In another case, which occurred in the South, two mentally retarded young African American girls were told that they were getting birth control medication but instead were sterilized by the government without their knowledge or permission. Mental patients who are subject to episodes of violence have either been kept totally sedated on drugs or subjected to brain surgery, both of which eliminate their violent episodes but also transform them into virtual zombies. In some cities, hyperkinetic children have not been allowed to go to school unless their parents have agreed to give them a drug that slows their level of activity—but which may also have questionable side effects.

Some prisoners and mental patients are kept sedated so that they can be controlled more easily in understaffed institutions. People who are subject to depression are sometimes given electroshock therapy or have electrodes implanted in their brains that, when stimulated, eliminate the depression—again with possible questionable side effects. Many people have sought to eliminate "bad habits" such as drinking alcohol, taking drugs, and overeating by going to clinics where they are aversively conditioned (i.e., made to suffer physical or mental discomfort) for continuing the habit and are rewarded for stopping it. These are just a few of the many situations in which ethical issues of behavior control arise. Implied in all of them are various problems and concerns, and it is these that the next section of this chapter will attempt to clarify.

ETHICAL ISSUES AND PROBLEMS WITH BEHAVIOR CONTROL. Because much behavior control is subtle, we must question whether we have the right to change people's behavior whether they know it or not or whether they consent or not. Ardent probehaviorists would say "yes" for several reasons. They would insist that we have a good idea of what "normal behavior" is, and that when people don't conform to it, their behavior should be changed for their own good and the good of others. The farther away from the norm the behavior is, they would argue, the more drastic the control must be (e.g., a scolding might be sufficient for a child who swears, but brain surgery would have to be considered for an adult given to episodes of uncontrollable violence).

Strong antibehaviorists, or individualists, however, would disagree. They believe that we *don't* know what the standard for normal behavior is and that setting one arbitrarily would be highly dangerous. Individual freedom, uniqueness, and creativity are to be encouraged and prized, and if these are to exist, we must allow for some deviation from the norm. True, they say, some behaviors should be discouraged and some encouraged, but proper ethical procedures must be employed at all times. For example, simply because a person in a mental hospital is in favor of brain surgery to curb his violence does not necessarily mean that the doctors should comply with his wishes. According to the antibehaviorists, we must ask several important questions concerning the protection of such people's rights as individuals. For example, can they really know, if they are so mentally disturbed that they must be institutionalized, what they are consenting to? Are they competent to judge what is best for them in such situations?

Another question that comes up with relation to changing behavior is how far we can carry the use of rewards, bonuses, or punishments. Doesn't it constitute rather strong coercion to give a man a choice between three to six years in prison and castration, or to give an impoverished man in India a bonus for having himself sterilized? Can people be considered to "freely" consent when they are being forcibly or even subtly coerced by financial rewards or promises of freedom?

Yet another problem that arises involves the therapist or controller as well as the patient. First of all, who should such controllers be, and to whom should they be responsible? To the society in which they live? The institutions at which they work? Their government? Their patients? For example, if a homosexual who lives in a militantly heterosexual society comes to a therapist for help, what is the therapist's duty? Should he or she help the homosexual to adjust to this type of sexuality and to the possibility of ostracism by some segments of society, or should the therapist try to steer the homosexual toward heterosexuality? Therapists' decisions about their responsibilities affect their patients and, more indirectly, the rest of society.

Human Experimentation

Human experimentation means the use of human beings for experimental purposes for their own therapy, for the good of humanity in general, or for the purpose of advancing scientific knowledge. Why is the question of human experimentation even raised? Of course, arguments for the use of such experimentations can be made based upon the

In 2010, the U.S government publically apologized for testing the effectiveness of penicillin on nearly 700 Guatemalans from the years 1946 to 1948. During the study, U.S. health officials intentionally infected the unknowing participants (prison inmates, mental patients, and soldiers) with syphilis. The means of infection were exposure to open wounds, spinal injections, and even introducing infected prostitutes to prison populations. Once infected, the medical officials were able to test the effectiveness of penicillin in fighting the bacteria.

FIGURE 2 Guatemalan syphilis experiment.

promise of advancement in medical knowledge as it concerns human health. In fact, much of what we know now about human diseases and effective means of treating them were derived from forms of experimentation performed on humans. Few people would argue that the consequences of such experimentation (effective vaccinations, organ transplants, improved medications, positive and negative effectives of certain types of medical treatments, etc.) are morally problematic. However, the means by which these medical advancements are achieved continue to be debated issues within the medical community and society as a whole. See the following case (Figure 2).[11]

As with most ethical dilemmas, the issue of human experimentation is complex. The Guatemalan experiment is a clear example of why we need to critically examine the ethical implications of such experiments. For example, are we justified in performing hazardous experiments on unknowing participants if the results of the experiment lead to major medical breakthroughs? Is it always wrong to use a human being as a means to an end? The main questions raised here, then, are to what extent human beings can be experimented upon and under what conditions and to what degree must they be informed about and freely consent to such experimentation.

THE PROEXPERIMENTATION ARGUMENT.   Those who take a strong proexperiment stance believe that as long as a specific experiment can advance scientific knowledge or aid humanity in some way, human experimentation is justified. People who are to be experimented on should be informed just enough so that they know something about what's being done to them, but not enough to interfere with the outcome of the experiment.

People in prison or in mental institutions who are willing to participate should be allowed to volunteer to aid humanity; in this way, they can make up for their previous crimes or their present uselessness. As an incentive, such people can be offered rewards (e.g., parole, release, or a better living situation). It is, further, even justifiable to experiment on institutionalized children or on children whose parents have given consent, in order to cure them when nothing else has worked or to benefit future children with similar problems.

THE ANTIEXPERIMENTATION ARGUMENT.   According to this point of view, human beings generally should not be used for experimentation. If science can't advance its knowledge by using animals, it simply cannot be advanced. No experimental drug or procedure should be used on any human being unless the following criteria are met: It is a last resort; it is meant to cure the person on whom it is used; the patient has given fully informed consent; and science has gone as far as it can with animal experimentation. Opponents of human experimentation point to the terrible experiments performed by doctors of Nazi Germany during World War II. Never again, these people argue, can science be given carte blanche to perform experiments on humans.

Furthermore, experimentation must never be done on human beings who are not mentally competent to consent, including people in mental institutions and all children, whether or not their parents are willing to consent. Experiments also must never be performed upon people who are not really free to consent, such as those incarcerated in prisons or other institutions. Finally, any human experimentation that is done, after all of these criteria have been satisfied, must also be extremely safe; it must not involve serious risk of illness, injury, or loss of life.

Immanuel Kant's Practical Imperative can be very useful here. Remember that the principle states that each human being must be considered as a unique end in himself or herself and never used merely as a means to someone else's end. In human experimentation, this would mean that no human being could be used for experimentation unless it would be therapeutic for that human being and would not be any more harmful or risky than other treatments that generally would be used for such patients. This would mean that no experimentation only for "the good of humanity or others" could be done. If this "good" were an indirect result of the experimentation, then it would be allowed, but the experimental procedure must be for the primary benefit of the patient on whom it is to be performed.

Many medical ethicists will follow this imperative as a guideline, but they may also allow experimentation when the person to be experimented on can give fully free and informed consent, realizing that the experiment may not be therapeutic for him or her, but for the good of humanity or the advancement of science. Where there is any doubt, however, the Practical Imperative forms a useful ethical criterion for human experimentation.

Genetics and Stem Cell Research

Genetics is that area of medicine and science which is concerned with the manipulation and control of the human genetic makeup. Research in genetics includes everything from discovering the causes of genetic problems and correcting such problems to creating human life in the laboratory. The main problem caused by genetics arises from determining how to use the technology we have to help us acquire genetic information and manipulate genes. It is obvious that this problem is very important, especially when we consider the potentially enormous effect of genetic manipulation upon individuals, families, and the overall gene pool.

There are, first of all, such procedures as amniocentesis and chorionic villus sampling, and other investigative and diagnostic procedures that can bring us important information about genetic defects or abnormalities. This information can, in turn, enable us to correct such deficiencies—if and when we can perfect the corrective procedures—or to avoid them altogether by means of either abortion or birth control, including sterilization. Genetic counseling is, therefore, intimately tied to important ethical questions.

Second, even more crucial ethical problems will arise as we approach the point at which we can correct and avoid genetic defects, cure diseases, or create life in the laboratory. Someday, we may even be in a position to decide what male and female types would best ensure the survival of the race and then reproduce them artificially. We could go even further and decide, as in Aldous Huxley's *Brave New World*, how many intellectuals, laborers, white-collar workers, and other types of people a "balanced, well-functioning society" needs and then create such a society in the laboratory.

At this point in scientific development these are somewhat exotic problems, but there is no reason to think that we will not be able to do these things in the future. Frogs and even mammals (e.g., sheep) have been cloned with some success. Also, scientists already have declared a moratorium on various types of experimentation having to do with creating life in the laboratory. As does human experimentation, the issue of genetic experimentation and development arouses strong opinions on both sides.

THE ARGUMENT FOR GENETIC EXPERIMENTATION AND DEVELOPMENT.   According to this argument, nothing and no one should stand in the way of advances in scientific knowledge and the chance to cure diseases or perfect the human race. The more we know about genetics, the more we can improve the human race and condition, and the better things will be. This betterment should be our primary goal; we should not worry about such trivial matters as the effects of experimentation upon the gene pool, or whether our information and abilities will result in abortion, sterilization, the elimination of defects, or the ability to create life in the laboratory. Self-imposed moratoriums and laws that prevent scientific advancement cannot be justified.

THE ARGUMENT AGAINST GENETIC EXPERIMENTATION AND DEVELOPMENT.   According to this argument, in the case of anything that tampers with the natural life process or interferes with God's or nature's plan, no scientific experimentation in this area, especially the artificial creation of life, should be allowed. Nature or God had a purpose in allowing some imperfections to exist in the human species, and tampering with this purpose could prove disastrous, not only to the natural development and progress of humanity but also to its moral and spiritual development. Nature or God has placed upon this earth human beings with handicaps and genetic problems to help us recognize that human imperfections do exist and also to encourage us to love and care for less fortunate human beings. If we create completely perfect human beings and eliminate all of those with imperfections, we will lose our humanity, both from a biological-physical and a moral-spiritual point of view.

STEM CELL RESEARCH

One of the most controversial types of genetic research today is stem cell research. Stem cells, the so-called master cells of the body, have the potential to become many different kinds of cells. They are the means by which cells in the body can be replenished. In the very early embryo, these cells have the power to become any kind of body cell. Adult stem cells, on the other hand, have the capacity to become a variety of cells, but not all kinds. They are difficult to obtain and very hard to coax into developing into other tissues; consequently, their use would involve much more time and money to obtain the desired results. Scientists hope to obtain lines of the embryonic cells, that is, large numbers of them grown from a common source and coax them into becoming specific kinds of cells. The desire of these scientists is to use stem cells to repair damaged tissues in the body, such as heart tissues to repair damaged hearts and nerve tissues to repair damaged spinal columns or reverse the effects of Alzheimer's or Parkinson's diseases.[12]

THE MORAL ISSUE OF USING EMBRYONIC STEM CELLS.   Although embryonic stem cells are much easier to use than adult stem cells, the moral issue for many, especially strong antiabortionists such as the Catholic Church, is that the procedure of extracting stem cells from a five- to seven-day-old embryo kills the embryo. Many pro-life people argue if we allow this, we do not respect human life (assuming that human life begins at fertilization of the egg by sperm—the strong pro-life point of view) and what is done is tantamount to abortion or the murder of human life in the embryonic stage. The moral dilemma occurs because scientists figure they can use such cells to develop tissues which can be used in curing chronic, disabling diseases such as Parkinson's, Alzheimer's, diabetes, and spinal cord injuries.

GOVERNMENT LIMITS.   President George W. Bush, faced with this dilemma and torn between his pro-life views against abortion and yet the desire to cure various diseases, said that federal funds will be used only for research on existing stem cell lines that were derived (1) with the consent of the donors; (2) from excess embryos created for reproductive purposes; and (3) without any financial inducement to the donors. No federal funds will be used for (1) stem cell lines derived from newly destroyed embryos; (2) the creation of human embryos for research purposes; or (3) the cloning of human embryos. The irony of his plan is that it satisfies neither the scientists, who want greater freedom and financial support for research, nor the pro-life supporters. Bishop Joseph A. Fiorenza, president of the U.S. Conference of Catholic Bishops, states the pro-life position when he said, "The trade-off he [Bush] has announced is morally unacceptable. It allows our nation's research enterprise to cultivate a disrespect for human life."[13] Scientists are disappointed because there are only a few stem cell lines available under Bush's plan, which, of course, drastically limits their research. Some states, such as New Jersey and California, have passed legislation legalizing stem cell research with fewer limitations than Bush's plan and with financial support coming from private, or nongovernmental, sources.

POSSIBLE SOLUTION. The latest research has shown that adult stem cells can be isolated and developed. If such research continues to be successful, there may be no reason whatsoever to use embryonic stem cells, which, of course, would resolve the dilemma.[14] It remains to be seen how long such research will take and whether scientists are willing to wait until the research is successful or whether they will deem the adult stem cells as useful as embryonic ones.

The Ethics of Body Trading and Tissue Banking

Rapid progress in biotechnology has outpaced regulation, and the public, too, lacks an awareness of, and understanding about, a highly lucrative global industry of body trading: body part buying, selling, retrading, and transplanting. Staggering advances in biotechnology and medical science concerning new uses for human tissue have given rise to a host of ethical, legal, and political issues that accompany the commercial enterprise of body trading. Altruistic donors, through ignorance, are routinely exploited, and relatives are stunned, dumbfounded, and outraged to learn that their loved ones have become products in the profitable tissue commerce business.

In addition to organ transplants, approximately 650,000 Americans each year undergo surgery that uses soft tissues, skin, bones, and tendons taken from cadavers. But, there are serious issues about the clandestine nature of body part procurement and a range of possible risks associated with product lines. Companies that process human tissue purchase body parts from hospitals, universities, and other institutions to which bodies are donated in good faith for research purposes. Procurement of bodies from Third World nations is even more problematic. A cadaver often generates over $200,000.00 in market value. Tissue companies reap high profits and trade on the global exchanges. Much of this industry is market driven, and shareholders place pressure on management to show profits quarter after quarter.

Due to lack of regulation (much of the industry in America is still governed by Blood Shield laws passed in the 1950s and 1960s), there are a number of product risks. Tissue can transmit the following to a transplant host: hepatitis, HIV, mad cow disease, bacteria, and other communicable diseases. There is also a failure to disclose information about the cadaver's lifestyle, sexual habits, prior illness, and whether he or she was a smoker, drinker, or drug user. Furthermore, there is not adequate research concerning the ways a cadaver's former lifestyle might impact the transplant host.

There is a need for better global regulation of, and public disclosure and transparency within, the body trading industry. Ethical, legal, and social issues must be more clearly defined in those cases that determine the status of body parts.

Cases for Study and Discussion

CASE 1 67-Year-Old Cancer Patient

Richard is a 67-year-old man with terminal cancer. He has just had a liver scan and been told to visit his doctor, an oncologist (i.e., a cancer specialist whose work focuses on tumors), and get the results. When Richard arrives, the doctor says that there has been no change in his condition, which is, nevertheless, not good. Richard asks the doctor what can be done, and he replies that there is no remedy for this kind of cancer. Becoming somewhat agitated, Richard asks the doctor what he would advise him to do, but the doctor merely repeats his opinion that there is nothing to be done. By this time Richard is both frustrated and upset, and he asks the doctor why he won't care for him and doesn't care about him. In response the doctor gives Richard a prescription, but he makes it clear that the drug is being prescribed only as a psychological crutch—that it will not improve Richard's health. When Richard finally leaves the doctor's office, he feels totally depressed, abandoned, and dehumanized. Do you feel the doctor handled Richard's case well? If so, why; if not, why not? How would you have handled the situation or advised the doctor to handle it? Discuss both the truth-telling aspect of what the doctor said and his methods of giving out information relating to his patient.

CASE 2 Abortion for Reasons of Gender of the Embryo

A middle-aged wife became pregnant and underwent amniocentesis testing to see if the baby would have Down syndrome. When the procedure was over, the genetic counselor was happy to inform the prospective parents that their baby would be quite healthy. She also told them, however, that the sex of the child was female. The husband and wife then decided to have an abortion because they already had several daughters, and the genetic counselor was beside herself with shock and concern. She felt that she might have done the wrong thing by revealing the sex of the child to the parents—that if she had merely told them about the Down syndrome results, they would not have decided on an abortion. Should the counselor have withheld the information about the sex of the child? Do the parents have a right to know all of the information disclosed by amniocentesis, only the information that is crucial to the health of the child, or only the information for which they ask? In short, what are counselors' obligations in revealing the results of such tests?

CASE 3 Videotaping Patients

A psychologist wants to videotape some of his patients during their therapy sessions, partly for a study he is doing and partly as a teaching device for advanced psychology students. He feels that if the patients know they are being taped, they won't act naturally, which will both taint his study and diminish the film's value as a teaching device. For this reason, he feels that the patients should not know that they are being taped even though what they do or say on the tape may reveal certain aspects of their private feelings and lives. What should the psychologist do? Should he tell the patients he is taping them, or should he just go ahead and tape without their permission, assuming that he is just going to use the tapes for his own research and as a teaching device? Are there any other alternatives you can think of for the psychologist to follow?

CASE 4 Experimenting on Children

A doctor-researcher in residence at a private institution for mentally retarded children discovers that the children in one of the dormitories have dysentery, whereas those in the other dormitories do not. She decides to experiment with the children, both to see what has caused this particular phenomenon and to study the effects of dysentery and its various cures upon children in general. She sets up a scientific study with control groups (in which some students receive medication and some do not), and part of her experiment involves infecting healthy children with dysentery germs. The institution for which she works has a long waiting list, and the doctor takes advantage of this, admitting only those children whose parents will sign a release allowing her to conduct experiments upon them. What are the ethical implications of what the doctor is doing? Should such experimentation be allowed? Why, or why not?

CASE 5 Homosexual Seeking Help

John, 25, comes to a psychiatrist very depressed about his homosexuality. He has had two heterosexual relationships, neither of which was satisfactory, and numerous homosexual ones, some of which were satisfactory and some of which were not. He also has used his homosexuality as a means of getting jobs, money, and other benefits. John is not quite sure what he wants to do about his homosexuality, but he does know that he is not very happy the way he is. What should the psychiatrist do? Should he try to help John become a heterosexual? Should he try to get him to adjust to his homosexuality? Discuss both of these alternatives, and describe the psychiatrist's responsibilities to himself, to John, and to society in general.

CASE 6 Woman in a Mental Institution

Mary, 45, is in a mental institution, on a ward for violent people. She is given to episodes of extreme violence during which she loses all control and becomes very dangerous. Between such episodes, she remembers at least some of what she has done, but when one of these episodes comes on, she just can't seem to stop or control it. There doesn't seem to be anything physiologically wrong with her brain, but a doctor suggests to her that she have a surgery performed that will eliminate her violence.

The doctor explains that this operation may cause extreme loss of memory—to the extent that Mary could read a newspaper and immediately forget everything she has read. Furthermore, the operation will make Mary so passive that she probably will not want to do very much with the rest of her life; however, after undergoing such an operation, she probably could be released from the institution. Mary is so deeply distressed by her violent episodes that she signs a release to have the surgery performed.

Describe the implications of informed consent in this case, and discuss Mary's ability to give it freely as an inmate of a mental institution. Also, discuss the extent to which coercion exists in the doctor's promise that Mary's violent episodes will end and in the suggestion that she may be released from the institution. Can Mary fully understand what she is agreeing to? And even if she does not fully understand, because she hasn't been cured by other methods, should she be allowed the brain surgery as a viable alternative or not?

CASE 7 Prisoner and Heart Transplant

Recently a 31-year-old twice-convicted robber became the first California state prisoner—and likely the first in the United States—to receive a heart transplant, a scarce and expensive resource. He suffered from a viral infection that had damaged his heart valves. He experienced congestive heart failure and was placed higher on the list because of his urgent medical condition. Many people, including some ethicists, thought that taxpayers shouldn't spend $1 million on a convict who was serving a 14-year sentence for a violent felony. Others, again including ethicists, thought that no distinction should be made between a convicted felon and anyone else who needed a heart transplant. In 1976, the U.S. Supreme Court ruled that prisoners must receive adequate medical care. One of the biggest problems in heart transplantation is the many medications necessary to prevent the body from rejecting the new heart and biopsies necessary during the first year following the surgery. This difficulty became apparent in this case in that the inmate died within the first year. The comment was made by the prison warden that prisoners generally don't take care of themselves and often don't take their medications. Do you think that major medical care, such as transplants, should be performed on prisoners? Why or why not? Would it make any difference if they were on death row, serving life sentences without parole, or serving determinate sentences, such as this inmate? Support your position with logical argument and proof.

CASE 8 Stem Cell Research

Do you think that stem cell research should be allowed to continue from embryos and/or adults? Why or why not? Support your answer with proof and logical argument. Should the government subsidize such research? Why or why not? If you agree that embryos should be used, which kind? Those from aborted fetuses? Leftover embryos from fertility processes? Should embryos be raised for research purposes? Why or why not?

Chapter Summary

I. Introduction and definition of terms
  A. *Bioethics* literally means "life ethics," or ethics in medicine.
  B. Bioethics covers the areas of caring for the dying; allowing someone to die, mercy death, and mercy killing; human experimentation and informed consent; genetics, fertilization, and birth; health care and its costs; population and birth control, abortion, and sterilization; allocation of scarce medical resources; and truth telling and confidentiality in medicine.
  C. It is essentially concerned with the establishment and maintenance of vital and moral human relationships between the sick and the dying and the healthy and the professional.

II. Health care personnel and patients and their families—rights and obligations
  A. Paternalism is the position that professionals should take a parental role toward patients and their families.
    1. Laypeople don't know what's best for them; therefore, they should place themselves totally in the hands of professionals because they and they alone have the proper medical background.
    2. Patients and their families are essentially like children when it comes to medical problems, so the professionals should serve as father figures.
    3. There are two possible models under paternalism:
       (a) The engineering model, in which the physician tries to be an applied scientist who is value free. The problem here is that physicians cannot logically be value free.
       (b) In the priestly model—which is the opposite extreme—the physician is a new priest. The problem is that he or she is still making decisions for the patient.
  B. Radical individualism is the position that patients should have absolute rights over their bodies and lives and may therefore reject doctors' recommendations.
    1. Doctors are nothing more than humans with special training, and therefore are capable of making errors.
    2. Patients and their families are better qualified than anyone else to make decisions concerning their own treatment because their bodies and lives are at stake.
    3. Many issues having to do with treatment are not strictly medical, and professionals are not qualified to make decisions about them.

4. Many lay people these days are quite knowledgeable about their bodies and about medicine, and even when they are not, they can be made to understand the nature of their medical problems when these are explained clearly and in plain language.

5. Paternalism often has led to total patient dependence on doctors and sometimes has resulted in dehumanization.

6. Problems with this model are that patients may not be qualified or knowledgeable enough to make decisions on their own; also, many patients don't want to be entirely responsible for such decisions.

C. The reciprocal model utilizes the team approach, in which patients and their families work with health care personnel to do what is best for patients.

1. Professionals are not gods or even father figures; they are merely human beings with specialized training.

2. Many decisions are not strictly medical; therefore, they should not be made strictly by professionals. Doctors need to rely on other support personnel (nurses, therapists, etc.) as well as nonmedical personnel, such as social workers, clergy, and trained volunteers in order to properly care for patients and their families as whole persons.

3. This view recognizes the importance of individual patients' rights in all medical areas.

4. It accepts the idea that neither patients nor professionals alone "know best" but that decisions should be reciprocal (involving give and take) rather than dictatorial, paternalistic, or anarchistic.

5. Patients are entitled to know what is happening to them, and decisions should be arrived at through a free exchange of ideas and be made jointly by everyone on the team.

6. There are two models under the reciprocal view:

   (a) The collegial model, in which the physician and patient see themselves as colleagues pursuing a common goal. The problem with this model is whether physicians and patients really can assume mutual loyalty and goals of common interest, given all their differences.

   (b) The contractual model is supposed to permit moral equality between physician and patient, without indulging in any utopian assumption of collegiality. The problems associated with this model are how to execute the contract and what to include in it.

III. Truth telling and informed consent

A. The main issue here is to what extent patients and their families should be told the truth about their medical situations and to what extent they should not.

B. *Informed consent* is a formalized procedure in which patients or their families consent in writing to medical procedures involving some degree of risk to their health or lives.

C. The paternalistic view holds that because patients are not medically trained, they cannot understand what doctors tell them; therefore, they do not need to know more than that professionals are doing their very best for them.

1. It is best for patients' morale and their will to get better or will to live that they aren't told bad news.

2. Keeping patients in the dark allows them to live the remainder of their lives without worry, concern, or depression; telling them bad news will not keep them from dying.

3. It is all right to tell the bad news to the families, but not to the patients.

4. Professionals and patients' families should avoid being morbid and should try to cheer up patients.

D. There are several arguments supporting the position that patients have a right to know about their condition.

1. They have a right to know because it is their bodies and lives that are at stake.

2. It is much easier to deal with patients who are aware of what is going on, as this makes pretense unnecessary.

3. Patients often are angry and feel dehumanized if they don't know what is going on or aren't told what to expect.

4. This approach, however, may lead some professionals to be frank to the point of being brutal or even cruel in telling patients the truth.

5. It is a false dilemma to assume that you have to either give people terrible news or lie to them.

6. A third view, the moderate position, which lies between paternalism and brutal frankness, favors the sharing of appropriate information when patients want and/or need to know it, letting the patients be the

guide as to how much information should be revealed. This involves the following:

(a) Listening to and really hearing patients.

(b) Answering patients' questions truthfully and compassionately.

(c) Not forcing information on patients but letting them decide what should be told and when it is to be told.

(d) Not avoiding questions or issues by means of employing technical medical language or jargon.

(e) Recognizing that explanations may have to be given in parts or more than once because of the shock of the news and resultant patient denial.

(f) Always giving information clearly, gently, and humanely, never coldly, brutally, or cruelly.

(g) Never leaving patients and their families without some hope, even if it is only that the patients will be cared for and kept free of pain.

E. Informed consent is necessitated in our times by the increased use of complex technological tests, procedures, and surgeries, not only for therapeutic reasons but also for experimental purposes.

1. In the United States, patients must be informed of the risks involved in any procedures that are to be performed upon them.

2. The assumption behind this approach is that in order to intelligently consent to any procedure, patients must be fully informed; they also should consent in writing so as to avoid future confusions or legal problems.

3. Most informed consent forms do the following:

(a) Explain the procedure and its purpose clearly and in ordinary language.

(b) Explain what the procedure will cause the patient to feel in the way of discomfort or pain before, during, and after the procedure.

(c) Explain any and all complications that may arise because of the procedure.

(d) State how long the procedure will take.

(e) Include a statement that the patient's doctors have judged the procedure to be so important to the patient's well-being that the risks involved are justified.

4. Several factors that could inhibit informed consent are illnesses or injury of the patient; various medications; physicians' and patients'

attitudes (arrogance versus submissiveness); and power asymmetries.

5. Often the best approach is for the physician to provide information in person as well as providing a consent form for the patient to read and sign; this will help to ensure full understanding and truly informed consent.

F. Doctors vary greatly in their reactions to truth telling and informed consent.

1. Doctors who generally are against both full disclosure of the truth and informed consent support their position with a number of arguments.

(a) Doctors know what they are doing, and having to explain complicated medical procedures to patients will only confuse the patients and break down the relationship of faith and trust between doctor and patient.

(b) Patients often really don't want to know the truth, and forcing it upon them against their wills both invades their privacy and is bad for their morale.

(c) Every procedure has its risks, but there is no reason to frighten patients unnecessarily, especially when the risks are very slight.

(d) Patients may be unnecessarily frightened to the point where they will refuse to have the necessary procedures performed.

(e) Unnecessary side effects also may be brought on by the power of suggestion.

2. Some doctors, on the other hand, have gone overboard in giving information whether or not the patients want to hear it, thus causing unnecessary anxiety.

G. The reactions of patients and their families to truth telling and informed consent also vary.

1. Some patients, and their families, don't want to know the truth because they wish to continue denying their problems. However, most patients do want to know what is happening to them; perhaps they don't need to know everything, but they certainly want to know the crucial facts.

2. That patients and their families want to deny their problems doesn't necessarily mean they don't want to know the truth. After all, there may be unfinished business to take care of, and knowing the truth may help all of them take care of it.

3. A great deal of sensitivity is necessary on the part of the whole health care team to know how, what, when, and where to tell the truth.

H. There are a number of guides to truth telling and informed consent.

1. Generally, patients and their families should be kept as fully informed as possible, especially when they clearly want to know the truth.

2. They should be dealt with truthfully, honestly, and compassionately and without cruelty, coldness, or brutal frankness.

3. If they consistently indicate that they don't want to know the truth, and if ignorance will do no harm to them or their families, then one can avoid telling them until they do want to know.

4. If patients want to know the truth but their families don't want them to, then the patients' desire should come first.

IV. Confidentiality

A. Generally the matter of confidentiality seems fairly clear in that what goes on between doctors and patients should always be confidential. Usually, this is the case.

B. The problems with HIV testing and AIDS have, however, made the matter of confidentiality a difficult issue in the following cases:

1. Spouses and partners deserve to be protected.

2. Patients deserve to be protected from health caregivers infected with HIV or AIDS.

C. As a general rule, confidentiality should be maintained, but at the same time everything must be done to protect the innocent from any kind of contagion.

1. People who are capable of infecting others must take the responsibility for warning them.

2. Where they won't or can't, confidential action must be taken in order to protect the innocent.

V. Guilt and innocence in treating patients

A. Often it is difficult for health care professionals to be objective in treating patients who have certain problems that have also been personal problems for the professionals in some way (e.g., a child abuser who needs treatment and a doctor or nurse who is the parent of a small child).

B. Another aspect of this issue arises when professionals have to keep treating patients who continuously abuse their own health (e.g., alcoholics).

C. This issue has become even more of a problem since the advent of AIDS.

D. It is not the job of health professionals to try, judge, or convict any patient of crimes, no matter how heinous. It is their job, rather, to treat sick or injured patients no matter what their background or lifestyle.

E. Professionals need not like such patients or condone what they have done or how they live, but neither must they let their own preconceptions or feelings enter into the quality of their treatment.

VI. Ethical issues in medicine

A. Ethics and behavior control is that aspect of bioethics that deals with general questions concerning the extent to which the behavior of human beings should be controlled by the various technologies available to us.

1. Several specific questions arise in relation to this issue:

(a) How do we determine what constitutes undesirable or socially unacceptable behavior?

(b) Which means of behavior control should be considered ethical, and which should not?

(c) Who should determine when behavior control is to be used?

2. Behavior control is the modification or changing of human behavior—with or without permission and with or without forcible or subtle coercion—by means of various technologies; drugs; psychotherapy; behavior modification techniques (reward or aversive conditioning); electrical brain stimulation (EBS); hypnotism; biofeedback; brain surgery; and incarceration.

3. The major problem here is that any control of behavior involves an encroachment upon or even an elimination of individual freedom; the question, then, is to what extent this should be allowed.

4. There are many ethical issues and problems associated with behavior control.

(a) Because much behavior control is subtle, we must question whether we have the right to change people's behavior whether they know it or not or whether they consent to it or not.

(b) Probehaviorists would say that we have this right because we know what normal behavior is, and those in society who can't conform to these norms ought to have their behavior changed.

(c) Antibehaviorists would say that we do not have this right because we don't know what the norm is, and setting one arbitrarily would be highly dangerous. Individual freedom, uniqueness, and creativity should be prized and protected at all costs.

(d) There are also questions concerning how far we can carry rewards, bonuses, or punishments when attempting to change or control behavior.

(e) We must ask ourselves to whom controllers should be responsible.

B. Human experimentation is the use of human beings for experimental purposes, either for their own therapy, for the good of humanity, or to advance scientific knowledge.

1. Experimentation eventually must be done on human beings because science can only go so far with animal experimentation.

2. The main question concerns the extent to which human beings can be experimented upon and under what conditions. Another important question concerns the extent to which people should be informed and freely consent to such experimentation.

3. There are two highly divergent viewpoints on this issue:

(a) Proponents of experimentation believe that as long as an experiment can advance scientific knowledge or aid humanity in some way, human experimentation is justified.

(b) Opponents of human experimentation believe that human beings should never be used for experimentation unless protective criteria are met because of the ease with which the rights of people whose freedoms are limited (prisoners, mental patients, and children) can be abused.

4. Immanuel Kant's Practical Imperative—that each human being must be considered as a unique end in himself or herself and never used merely as a means to someone else's end—can be useful here.

(a) A person generally should not be experimented on unless the experimental procedure is therapeutic and not harmful.

(b) A person may be experimented on provided he or she is fully informed and can freely consent to such experimentation, realizing that it may not be therapeutic to himself or herself but good for humanity.

C. Genetics is the area of bioethics that is concerned with the manipulation and control of the human genetic makeup.

1. The main problem created by genetics is in determining how to use the technology we have acquired for gaining genetic information and manipulating genes, especially when we consider the possibly deleterious effect of genetic manipulation upon individuals, families, and the overall gene pool.

2. Procedures such as amniocentesis and chorionic villus sampling provide us with information that forces us to make decisions concerning birth control, abortion, and sterilization.

3. As our technology increases we can correct genetic deficiencies, create life in the laboratory, and clone ideal human beings. This raises questions as to whether we should do any of these things and, if so, to what extent. Also, what effect will this technology have on the human species?

4. There are two highly divergent viewpoints on genetic experimentation and development.

(a) Supporters of genetic experimentation and development believe that nothing and no one should stand in the way of scientific advancement and the chance to perfect the human race because the world can only benefit from such improvements.

(b) Opponents of genetic experimentation and development believe that anything that tampers with the natural life process, interfering with nature's or God's plan, should be prohibited. This includes scientific experimentation in the area of genetics, especially the artificial creation of life.

D. Stem cell research is one of the most controversial types of genetic research.

1. Stem cells are master cells of the body and can be obtained from both adults and human embryos.

2. The moral issue with using embryonic stem cells is that the embryo is killed during the procedure.

3. President Bush has authorized federal funds for a very limited use of embryonic cells.

4. Some states have made stem cell research legal and intend to use private funds if the government will not subsidize the research.

E. Rapid progress in biotechnology has outpaced regulation and public awareness of a highly lucrative global industry of body trading: body part buying, selling, retrading, and transplanting.

1. There are serious issues about the clandestine nature of body part procurement and the enormous profits generated in the process.

2. Due to lack of regulation there are product health risks to a transplant host including hepatitis, HIV, mad cow disease, bacteria, and other communicable diseases.

3. There is both a lack of information about and a failure to disclose risks about a cadaver's former lifestyle, sexual habits, prior illness, and whether he or she was a smoker, drinker, or drug user.

4. Issues of regulation and transparency must be addressed in the growing enterprise of body trading and tissue banking.

✓●─ **Study** and **Review** on **mythinkinglab.com**

Exercises for Review

1. Investigate and research one of the areas of bioethics not covered in this chapter (e.g., organ transplantation), and write or give an oral report on your research following your instructor's guidelines.

2. Outline in detail what you feel are the rights and obligations of doctors, nurses, patients, families, chaplains, and hospitals, and discuss whether these relationships should be paternalistic, radically individualistic, or reciprocal. How do you feel about Veatch's four models? If you were a patient, which model would you choose?

3. To what extent do you think the truth about terminal illness should be told to patients and their families? Why?

4. Describe the difference between "informed consent" and general truth telling, and design an informed consent form for some procedure, experiment, interview, or task you might want people to participate in. Explain in detail what you expect them to do; then describe the methods you would use to help them to understand the project so that they could give their informed consent to it. Explain how you would protect them from exposing their private lives or endangering themselves or their reputations.

5. To what extent and under what circumstances do you feel that people's behavior should be controlled? Do you feel that it is acceptable to control people in such a way that they don't know they are being controlled? Why or why not?

6. To what extent do you feel that reward, punishment, or other types of forcible or subtle coercion should be used to get people to behave in certain ways?

7. If someone is in a position to control behavior (e.g., a teacher or a psychotherapist), to whom should he or she be responsible and to what degree?

8. To what degree do you believe that human beings can or should be experimented on? Under what conditions would you allow such experimentation? What safeguards or guidelines would you establish and enforce to protect both the subjects being experimented upon and the experimenters? Why?

9. Discuss at length the extent to which you would allow behavior control and experimentation to be performed upon children with or without their parents' permission. Support your position in detail.

10. To what extent do you feel that genetic experimentation and development should be allowed, especially experiments that involve the creation of human life in the laboratory, stem cell research, and the cloning of human beings? Answer in detail, providing evidence and supporting arguments for your position.

11. Research the case described in Figure 2. How might Kant's Practical Imperative ("Act to treat humanity, whether yourself or another, as an end-in-itself and never as a means.") help us to critique the kind of human experimentation that went on in Guatemala?

12. John C. Cutler was the public health official who led the Guatemalan experiment (Figure 2). Later, he would play a significant role in the syphilis experiments in Tuskegee where African American men who had contracted syphilis were observed for the physiological effects of the bacteria. However, they were left untreated. When asked about the nature of the Tuskegee experiment, Cutler stated, "It was important that they were supposedly untreated, and it would be undesirable to go ahead and use large amounts of penicillin to treat the disease, because you'd interfere with the study." How does Cutler's view coincide with the *Pre/experimentation Argument?*

13. In 1946, the year the Guatemalan experiments began, the Nuremburg Tribunals commenced in trying Nazi doctors for heinous experiments done on victims in concentration camps. Research the Nuremburg Code. Was this code taken into consideration in Guatemala or Tuskegee experiments? Should someone like John C. Cutler, who was involved in both the Guatemalan and Tuskegee experiments, be put on trial for crimes against humanity?

14. Do you think that stem cell research should be allowed to continue from embryos and/or adults? Why or why not? Support your answer with proof and logical argument. Should the government subsidize such research? Why or why not? If you agree that embryos should be used, which kind? Those from aborted fetuses? Leftover embryos from fertility processes? Should embryos be raised for research purposes? Why or why not?

15. How do you feel about the issue of moral guilt and innocence as these are perceived by health care professionals when they are treating patients? How do you suggest these professionals treat patients whom they consider to be guilty of terrible crimes or immoralities? What types of patients would you yourself find it difficult to treat, and why? How would you overcome your distaste for or hatred of them? Do you think that all patients deserve the best treatment health professionals can give them, regardless of what they have done or who they are? Why or why not? Explain in detail.

Views of the Major Ethical Theories on Bioethical Issues

Describe as fully as you can how each of the major ethical theories—Ethical Egoism, Utilitarianism, Divine Command Theory, Kant's Duty Ethics, Ross's *Prima Facie* Duties, and Virtue Ethics—probably would deal with the bioethical issues of the rights and obligations of health care personnel and patients; truth telling and informed consent; confidentiality; behavior control; genetics; and human experimentation.

Ethics Problem
Kidney for Sale on Craigslist

As a young college student, Jerry has found himself behind on several important bills. Faced with the reality of living without electricity, water, and gas, Jerry decided that drastic measures were required to settle his debt and establish economic stability until he finishes his college degree. Three months earlier Jerry's kidneys were tested for donor compatibility in order to save the life of his ailing father. Unfortunately, neither he nor anyone else on the donor lists matched. One month later, Jerry lost his father and his financial security. With his current financial crises and knowledge of both his blood and tissue type, Jerry decided to sell his kidney through an ad on Craigslist for $25,000. Within hours, his inbox was full of requests from potential buyers who were desperate for a transplant. Unfortunately for Jerry, he was informed that it was illegal for individuals to sell their own organs.

Research the National Organ Transplant Act. Why do you think such a law was needed? Do you believe people have just as much right to profit from selling personal organs as the Medical Industry? Do you think that commoditizing organ sales would help those awaiting organ transplants? What concerns might you have about the commoditization of human organs?

Notes

1. Robert Veatch, "Models for Ethical Medicine in a Revolutionary Age," *Hastings Center Report* (June 1972), 6.
2. Ibid.
3. Ibid., 7.
4. John A. Behnke and Sissela Bok, *The Dilemmas of Euthanasia* (Garden City, NY: Anchor Books, 1975), 157–59.
5. Some of these questions are mine, and some were taken from an Ann Landers column in *The Bakersfield Californian* (October 29, 1987), E8.
6. Veatch, "Models of Ethical Medicine," 8.
7. Ibid.
8. Ibid., 9.
9. Ibid.

10. See Barney G. Glaser and Anselm L. Strauss, *Awareness of Dying* (Chicago: Aldine, 1965), for the best presentation of the difficulty of maintaining the various types of pretense between the healthy and the professional and the sick and the dying.

11. McNeil Donald E., Jr., "U.S. Apologizes for Syphilis Tests in Guatemala," *New York Times on the Web*, October 1, 2010, http://www.nytimes.com/2010/10/02/health/research/02infect.html (accessed February 2, 2010).

12. Thomas A. Shannon, "Stem Cell Research," http://www.americancatholic.org/Newsletters/CU/ac0102.asp, 1–2.

13. *The Bakersfield Californian* (August 10, 2001), Al.

14. Shannon, "Stem cell Research," 2.

▶ Read the Document on mythinkinglab.com

"The Case for the Use of Animals in Biomedical Research," Carl Cohen.

Structure and Function of Cells

Dr. Torsten wittmann/SPL/Photo Researchers

Fluorescent light micrograph of fibroblast cells from connective tissue.

Current Issue

The Use of Human Stem Cells

What do boxing champion Muhammad Ali and actor Michael J. Fox have in common? They both suffer from Parkinson's disease, a debilitating neurological disorder. The key to curing Parkinson's disease and many other diseases and health problems including Alzheimer's disease, leukemia, diabetes, and spinal cord injuries may be **stem cells.**

A stem cell is a cell from which other types of more specialized cells originate (or stem). The ultimate stem cell is the fertilized egg, for *all* of the specialized cells of the body originate from it. The first eight cells of a human embryo are also

stem cells, since they have not yet begun to differentiate (become different from each other). But shortly after the eight-cell

David McNew/Getty Images, Inc.

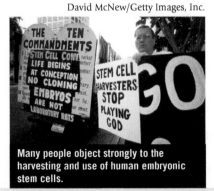

Many people object strongly to the harvesting and use of human embryonic stem cells.

stage the cells begin to specialize. Some become muscle; others become skin; still others become nerve cells in the brain.

Stem cells have several properties that make them desirable for research and for the treatment of certain diseases. They are easier to work with in the laboratory than adult cells because they don't adhere tightly to each other, and they grow better in culture (in controlled conditions, such as in a laboratory). They generally don't provoke a "tissue rejection" immune response in the patient because they are undifferentiated and thus not recognized as foreign cells. They are also easier to administer to a patient—usually they can be injected and allowed to migrate to their target site rather than having to be surgically transplanted. And most important, they still have the capacity to become the type of specialized cell the patient needs, under the direction of the patient's own cell division/differentiation control mechanisms.

Traditionally most human embryonic stem cells have come from very early-stage embryos. Currently, the only available embryos of this age are those created "in excess of clinical need" by *in vitro* fertilization at private fertility clinics. Only a few researchers have access to such embryos. However, cells used to treat specific diseases don't need to be completely undifferentiated. If nerve cells are needed, a good source of young cells is the very first embryonic neural tissue in the human fetus. Already, over 100 people with Parkinson's disease have received fetal nerve cell transplants worldwide, and some have shown measurable improvements in brain function. Nonliving human fetuses are widely available as a consequence of the more than one million legal abortions performed in the U.S. each year.

Controversy and Compromise

Not surprisingly, the use of human embryonic cells from fertilized eggs and undifferentiated fetal cells from legally aborted fetuses is highly controversial. On one hand, patient advocacy groups recognize the potential benefits of human embryonic and fetal cells and promote efforts to harvest and use them. On the other, some human rights groups object strongly to harvesting or using human embryonic stem cells or fetal cells under any circumstances, calling such research the destruction of precious human life. Both sides believe strongly in their position and both sides are active politically, and as a result politicians have been forced to take a stand.

According to guidelines developed under the Bush administration in 2001,

Muhammad Ali and Michael J. Fox, both sufferers of Parkinson's disease, support stem cell research.

federal funds could only be used to study stem cell lines derived from embryos before 2001. (A stem cell "line" is a group of identical cells grown from a single stem cell.) In effect, the 2001 federal guidelines prohibited the National Institutes of Health, which funds most biomedical research, from financing any stem cell research that might require the *future* death of a human embryo, but allows research on cells harvested from embryos in the past. However, the guidelines stopped short of prohibiting human stem cell research altogether; privately funded human embryonic stem cell research is still permitted under certain conditions.

The guidelines developed under President Bush were a political compromise at best. They allow selected federally funded research projects to go forward with the few stem cell lines that already existed at the time the law was passed (2001), while respecting concerns about the sanctity of human life. The guidelines were opposed by stem cell researchers, who contended that the limited number of cell lines available were not enough for the United States to stay in the forefront of this important research area. Some stem cell researchers moved to Britain, which had developed a facility for storing thousands of cell lines, or to other places in the world where stem cell research was not only allowed, but encouraged.

The election of President Obama changed the political environment yet again. Shortly after taking office in 2009,

President Obama signed an executive order lifting the restrictions on stem cell research laid down by President Bush. Federally funded researchers are now free to use the hundreds of stem cell lines in existence today, as well as new stem cell lines created by private funding in the future. But there is still a prohibition in place, called the Dickey-Wicker Amendment of 1996, which prohibits federal funding for research "in which human embryos are created, destroyed, discarded, or knowingly subjected to risk of injury or death." So while federally funded researchers will be able to use stem cell lines created by private funds (because the researchers themselves did not destroy any embryos), they will still be prohibited from creating their own new cell lines from human embryos. Obviously, the controversy over stem cells is not over.

What Is the Solution?

Both sides in this controversy actually do have something they can agree on; they both hope that someday we will not need to use stem cells from embryos or fetuses at all. The key may be the development of methods to create undifferentiated stem cells from fully differentiated adult cells—in essence, reversing the entire process of cellular differentiation and specialization. Several groups of scientists already claim to have done it successfully. But some scientists caution that new techniques for creating stem cell lines may not necessarily translate quickly into cures for specific diseases. It would be a shame if a well-meaning public, convinced that human embryonic stem cells are no longer necessary, came to accept laws that severely restrict human embryonic stem cell research in this country. Although the day may yet come when human embryonic stem cells truly aren't necessary, that day has not yet arrived. Just ask Michael J. Fox or Mohammed Ali.

Questions to consider

1 What is your opinion on this controversy? What basic beliefs do you hold that cause you to feel as you do?

2 Suppose that you and your spouse held frozen embryos at a private fertility clinic and that you knew you would never need them. Would you donate them for stem cell research? Why or why not?

The facts...

- Stem cells obtained from human embryos and fetuses have the potential to treat or cure diseases.

- Research using cells obtained from human embryos or fetuses is controversial.

- In the United States, stem cell research has been affected by changes in the political environment.

- In the distant future, human embryos and fetuses may no longer be needed as a source of stem cells.

Defining Death, Abortion, Stem Cells, and Animal Welfare: The Basis of Moral Standing

In the previous chapter we saw that different cultures and social groups have different medical ethical codes or oaths. One way or another they provide compilations of ethical principles, virtues, rules, or rights that specify the norms of morally right conduct and character. In addition to the question of which set of norms should be used, they must also address another major issue. To whom do these norms apply? That might seem to be a question with an obvious answer—they apply to human beings. The question is, however, far more complex. At least four problems arise.

First, some codes are written as if they apply only to members of certain professional groups. They delineate norms of conduct for physicians, nurses, or other health professionals. But even these raise troublesome questions. Are the writers claiming that they apply to all members of the relevant profession or only to those who are members of the organization that adopted the code? For example, the American Medical Association's (AMA) code prohibits active mercy killing. Does that prohibition apply to all physicians, even those who are not members of the AMA? Certainly, it does not make sense for it to apply to physicians who are not American. Also, some codes written by professional groups specify behavior that is morally required for patients and other lay people. Can these professional organizations claim authority to specify what is morally right conduct for those who are not even in the profession and cannot be members of these organizations? Can these norms be imposed on lay people who have no voice in creating them?

A second problem is that professional groups are not the only ones who write codes purporting to state norms of professional conduct. Religious groups and governmental agencies write them as well. One can imagine a religious group claiming authority to articulate norms for its physician members. It might even claim to know what the norms of conduct are for those who are not members of the religious body. Secular philosophies might make similar claims. Ethical norms are usually thought to be universal; that is, a single system of ethics applies to all. But there are many different groups claiming to know what those norms are. For example, since both religious and professional groups claim to be able to articulate the norms of conduct for physicians and other health professionals, a physician may feel he or she is subject to the norms articulated not only by the professional group, but also by his or her religion—and the two may not approve of or permit the same conduct.

Third, ethical duties in the biomedical world may extend beyond living human beings. In the era of organ transplantation, people may be seen as having moral duties regarding bodies of the newly dead. In the era of genetic manipulation, **stem cells**, and test tube babies, the same can be said for human gametes and embryos. There seem to be moral limits on how these are treated, even if they are not considered living human beings. Whether an embryo—or for that matter a fetus—has the same moral standing as (other) living human beings is a matter of enormous controversy. Whether the moral principles—such as the principle of beneficence or avoidance of killing—should apply (or could apply) to these entities with a human genetic endowment will require much more philosophical work. Also, some non-human animals appear to most people to have some kinds of moral claims on us. Those claims may not be as weighty, but they exist nonetheless. We need to understand to whom the principles apply—to which humans (if not to all) and to which beings that are not human (if any).

Finally, the very language of morality and moral standing is complex. We speak in casual conversation of humans, persons, individuals, and human beings, sometimes interchangeably and sometimes with important moral differences presumed or implied. We need to understand how these terms should be to be used in more careful ethical discourse. In this chapter we first look at these linguistic questions. Then we examine four major areas of biomedical ethics that play key roles in deciding to whom the moral principles apply and to what extent. We examine the debate about the definition of death to see when we believe we should quit treating a human as having the full moral standing that is attributed to normal humans. Following that, we look at the other end of life to the even more controversial area of abortion to see when we should begin treating humans as having full moral standing. The link between the two will quickly become clear. Third, since the writing of the second edition of this book, the new and controversial area of the use of stem cells has emerged. We will take up the aspects of the stem cell controversy related to moral standing. Finally, we look at the controversy over animals to see whether any non-human animals have moral standing and, if so, how much.

PERSONS, HUMANS, AND INDIVIDUALS: THE LANGUAGE OF MORAL STANDING

The Concept of Moral Standing

We need to identify those to whom the moral norms apply, that is, those who are owed duties of beneficence, nonmaleficence, and the other moral principles. One way of speaking is to refer to any being to whom we owe some kind of duty as having **moral standing**. We usually believe that humans (at least normal humans) have moral standing, but other animals may as well. Extremely abnormal humans also pose some difficult questions—the permanently unconscious and the severely retarded, for example. Nevertheless, most people believe these humans have moral claims as well. It is also widely believed that non-human animals are owed at least something. Almost everyone believes we should not cause them pain, certainly not without good reason. Whether we have a duty not to kill them is more controversial. Some people even believe that we have duties toward plants and inanimate objects.

Assuming we do have such duties toward non-human animals, plants, and inanimate objects, the reason we have them is the cause of further controversy. It may be because they are the possessions of another, in which case the moral claims may be indirect. Both religious and secular people often speak as if we have duties toward trees, ecological systems, or natural landscapes. For religious people, it may be because they believe that these are God's creation or God's possessions. For secular ecologists, the reasons why we have such duties are harder to articulate. It may be because other human beings have claims to enjoy the rest of nature, but often ecologists speak as if the duties toward the environment were more direct, that there is something intrinsically wrong with destroying a gene sequence even if humans have no interest in it and get no benefit from it. This may be because we believe that, even if these genes are not useful now, we may find that genetic material useful to humans in the future. Or it may be because it is intrinsically valuable and simply deserves protection.

Whenever we speak this way we can say that any animals, plants, and inanimate objects to which we owe some kind of duties have *moral standing*. Clearly, not all the moral principles can apply in each case, however. It is hard to imagine what it would mean, for example, to speak of a duty to respect the autonomy of trees or to tell the truth to them, although we can imagine what it might mean to have a duty to avoid killing them.

It is common to speak as if humans have a special moral standing. Some say that they each have maximum or "full" moral standing. Moreover, if each human has maximum standing, the standing of each is equal. Whatever duties we owe to them, we owe to them equally. Those who hold such a view would say that these humans have *full and equal moral standing*.

It is not that those outside this group have no standing at all. For example, it seems we owe lower animal such as rabbits something. At least we should not inflict pain on them without good reason. It appears that we can divide the world into those who have full standing and those to whom we owe some lesser duties. Most people, rightly or wrongly, tend to treat lower animals as having a lesser status. They would be quite willing to sacrifice a rabbit for the welfare of a human child, but unwilling to sacrifice a child for the welfare of rabbits, even if the amount of good we could do to the rabbits of the world was enormous. Likewise, if a human child and a bobcat were both starving and we have enough food only for one, certainly most people would favor giving the food to the child. (In fact, many would support killing the bobcat to feed to the child, but no one would favor killing the child to feed to the bobcat.) We can say of such special moral status that we give the child that he or she has full moral standing.

One of the critical questions in biomedical ethics is who has full moral standing. When we divide living beings into those with full standing and those with some lesser standing, there is a burden of justification when the time comes to draw the dividing line. It is that problem that is addressed in this chapter.

Moral and Descriptive Uses of the Term *Person*

The English language has done us a disservice by giving us so many ways of referring to humans while at the same time often lacking precision in how these terms are used. We speak of human beings, persons, and individuals, as well as using more technical terms such as "moral agents." In the field of ethics, sometimes these terms do important moral work, signifying our commitment that the being referred to either has or does not have some kind of moral standing. The language may signal that we have duties toward it as called for by the various ethical principles or that it has a particular type of moral standing. In other cases, however, these words can be used in a way conveying no moral implication at all. To make matters particularly confusing, sometimes the same word can be used both morally and nonmorally, even by the same speaker and in the same paragraph or sentence (see Figure 6).

PERSON DEFINED AS "THOSE WHO POSSESS CERTAIN PROPERTIES"   The word *person* is particularly confusing in this regard. Some times the word is used in ways that do not necessarily convey any moral status. Thus, a **person** can be *defined* as any self-aware or rational being. (Other physical or mental characteristics that do not necessarily imply a moral status are also sometimes used such as possessing an opposing thumb, a human genetic code, or self-awareness.) It should be clear that, if *person* is defined descriptively—that is, by citing one or more crucial properties such as self-awareness—nothing follows about whether such persons have moral status. One always needs some moral assumption to justify a conclusion about moral status. Likewise, those who lack the critical characteristic(s) could still have full moral standing. Thus, it could be a correct use of the language to say, "Even though a baby is not a person in the sense of possessing self-awareness, nevertheless, babies have full moral standing." Such a statement would simply convey that the speaker based moral standing on something other than that on which he or she bases personhood. Using the language in this way, we can say that there could be human living nonpersons with full moral standing. Likewise, although it would today be an unusual moral view, it would not be a linguistic contradiction to say that some individuals are persons in the sense that they possess self-awareness and yet they lack full moral standing. (Certain racists might hold such a view, for example.) Those who use the word *person* in this way are also using it in a nonmoral sense.

Person (nonmoral definition):

Humans (and other beings) who possess one or more critical physical or mental capacities such as self-awareness or rationality

Person (moral definition):

Humans (and other beings) who possess full or maximal moral standing

---

FIGURE 6   Two Definitions of Person

PERSONS DEFINED AS "THOSE WITH FULL MORAL STANDING" Making matters more confusing, others use the word *person* in a way that attributes moral standing to its referents *by definition*. According to this view, we must first determine who has full moral standing (and who does not) and then call all in the first group *persons*. Hence, one might say, "I believe that embryos have full moral standing and therefore are persons even though they obviously lack self-awareness." Or someone might say, "Even though small children possess self-awareness, they are nevertheless not *persons* because they do not have full moral standing." While this would be an unusual view about the moral status of children, if being a person means nothing more than having moral standing, it is a linguistically comprehensible statement. On the other hand, such a statement would be self-contradictory if the speaker defined *person* as meaning "one who possesses self-awareness."

The bottom line is that some use the term *person* to identify those with certain physical or mental characteristics, while others use the term to identify those who, by definition, have moral standing regardless of whether they possess any particular mental or physical characteristics.

CONFUSION RESULTING FROM SHIFTING FROM A NONMORAL TO A MORAL USE OF THE TERM *PERSON* The problem arises when someone tries to say something like the following:

> Late term fetuses are not persons because they lack self-awareness (or self-consciousness or ability to reason). But, since lacking personhood means one lacks full moral standing, fetuses can be aborted.

Whether it is ethical to abort fetuses is controversial. One cannot validly get to the conclusion that it is ethical by using the reasoning just presented. Using the nonmoral definition, the speaker first claims that fetuses are not persons. He or she wants us to accept as obvious that fetuses do not possess some key nonmoral characteristic such as self-awareness. Then the speaker shifts to the moral meaning of the term *person*, claiming that only persons have moral standing. Notice that, as long as one defines *person* without any reference to moral standing, one has not established that only persons have moral standing. This linguistic sleight of hand seems to suggest a proof that fetuses lack full moral standing, but it is merely a linguistic shift from a nonmoral to a moral definition of persons. What is not established in the two-sentence statement is that only those with self-awareness possess full moral standing and that, after all, is what the whole abortion debate is all about.

This confusion between the position that persons have moral standing by definition and the position that personhood can be defined based on certain nonmoral characteristics leads to enormous confusion in medical ethics debates. The easiest way to eliminate this confusion is simply to exclude the use of personhood language, requiring those arguing for one or another position about moral standing to make their claim in a straightforward way. Hence, if one wants to hold that fetuses lack moral standing, it won't do to claim that they are not persons and that only persons have standing. Or if one wants to hold that they possess moral standing, it won't do to claim that they are persons and therefore they must have moral standing. Either persons have moral standing by definition, in which case little is established, or persons possess some nonmoral physical or mental characteristics, in which case claiming someone is a person tells us nothing about their moral status without going on to show that these characteristics imply moral standing.

Proving that some nonmoral characteristic such as self-awareness or a unique genetic code is what it takes to establish full moral standing is extremely difficult to do. If such a link could be proved, someone would have done so by now and the abortion, definition of death, and animal rights debates would be over. Apparently, there are no definitive secular proofs of what characteristics establish full moral standing. Instead, we rely on firmly held beliefs—either secular or religious—that cannot be proved to others who do not share those beliefs. Nevertheless, virtually everybody accepts the idea that some beings have full moral standing while others do not. The inability to prove what characteristic establishes full moral standing is the reason why we continue to have controversy over the definition of death (when full moral standing ceases), abortion (when full moral standing begins), and the moral standing of non-human animals.

Moral and Nonmoral Uses of the Word *Human*

A similar problem arises with the use of the word *human*. Sometimes those who adopt liberal views on abortion will say that human life does not begin until quickening or the third trimester of gestation or even birth. Similarly, those who are skeptical about the moral standing of anencephalic infants or the persistently vegetative may claim that such beings are not "human." Clearly, they are not challenging the genetic makeup of such beings; they are merely making claims about their lack of full moral standing.

On the other hand, conservatives may respond by pointing out that these beings clearly are "human" since they possess the genetic code of the human species. (They are not cats or dogs.) In making these claims they are relying on our consensus that the anencephalics or fetuses or persistently vegetative adults in question possess some nonmoral characteristic that makes them a part of the human species. They trade on the consensus on the characteristics of humans defined nonmorally to attempt to establish that all those with these characteristics are also humans defined as having full moral standing. Once again, it seems that one can only add confusion by sliding from a nonmoral definition to one that establishes moral status by definition. Clearly, to be a human in a nonmoral sense establishes nothing one way or another about whether that being also has full moral standing. Doing so requires a belief that all who are humans in the nonmoral sense also possess full moral standing. Or, to point out the liberal's problem, establishing that one lacks some nonmoral characteristic of human-ness, such as self-consciousness, does not prove one lacks moral standing.

The issue in this chapter is how people have attributed moral standing to individuals and, further, how they have attributed what we call *full moral standing*.

DEFINING DEATH

It is probably best to start by examining what it means to lose full moral standing. A good case could be made that when there is a quantum change so that full moral standing is lost we say that the individual has died. That means that certain moral and legal rights that once applied to this individual no longer do. We, for instance, can no longer be guilty of killing such an individual. At least for humans, the fight over the definition of death is really a fight over when we should no longer treat someone the way we normally treat living humans. Once an individual is said to have died, our moral (and legal) duties toward that individual are not the same. One cannot "kill" a corpse. Other rights claims are also terminated. To say that someone has *died* therefore means, among other things, that we no longer attribute full moral standing to the individual. To be sure, even a corpse is thought to retain some attenuated moral standing. There are things we could do even to a corpse that would be considered immoral.

In Chapter 6 we will encounter the principle of avoiding killing. A critical problem with the principle of avoiding killing—the idea that it is wrong to kill people—is that we need to figure out what it means to be dead since, once we consider someone dead, killing is no longer relevant. Up until recently, we all knew who was dead and who was alive; it was straightforward. But in the last half century it has become increasingly difficult to decide whether someone is really dead or alive.

Remember Yusef Camp, the boy we encountered in Chapter 1 who ate the pickle and was left possibly brain dead in a hospital bed. If we cannot agree on whether he is dead or alive, we are going to have a real problem figuring out how to handle such a case. We need to determine whether the clinicians who favor cessation of treatment can stop on the grounds that their patient is deceased. Alternatively, they might have to claim that it is acceptable to stop treatment even though the patient is still alive.

There are three general positions regarding what it means to be dead (Capron, 2004; Controversies in the Determination of Death: A White Paper by the President's Council on Bioethics, 2008; Lamb, 1985; Law Reform Commission of Canada, 1979; President's Commission for the Study of Ethical Problems in Medicine and Biomedical and Behavioral Research, 1981). These are defined in Figure 7.

A Somatic Definition of Death

The first, the traditional definition, can be called the *somatic definition of death* (Jonas, 1974; Shewmon, 2001). According to this view, an individual dies when there is irreversible loss of the body's capacity to carry on integrated functioning. Usually the

Cardiac-Oriented

Irreversible loss of cardiac and respiratory function

Whole-Brain-Oriented

Irreversible loss of all function of the entire brain

Higher-Brain-Oriented

Irreversible loss of higher-brain functions (those responsible for consciousness of other functions consider crucial)

FIGURE 7 Three Definitions of Death

focus is on cessation of circulatory and respiratory function, but the body also carries on other complex, integrated functions having to do with such complex processes as digestion, elimination, reproduction, and maintaining homeostasis. What holders of this view consider essential is that a body is alive as long as it can carry out complex, integrated maintenance of the body as a whole. Thus, we can refer to this view as the somatic integration view. Sometimes (recognizing that heart function is one crucial element in bodily integration) this is simply referred to as a **cardiac-oriented definition**, keeping in mind that we are referring not just to the functioning of the heart, but also to the functioning of the circulatory and respiratory systems as well as other bodily systems. A minority of the U.S. President's Council on Bioethics (2008, p. 90) support this definition of death based on irreversible loss of somatic integration. One can infer from a study published in 2004 that about 14 percent of Ohio citizens held this minority view (Siminoff, Burant, and Youngner, 2004).

It is clearly possible for someone to be alive with a dead heart—even under this definition of death. As the following case shows, those who favor this definition can recognize that an individual can be alive even if his heart is totally removed and discarded.

CASE 3

The Man Living Without a Heart

Some year ago, a dentist named Barney Clarke was a heart patient at the University of Utah, where clinicians were experimenting with artificial hearts. Since he was at death's door and awaiting a heart transplant, the physicians removed his heart and connected his aorta and veins back up to a Jarvik-7 artificial heart pump. Barney Clarke lived for four months on that artificial heart. At times he was doing quite well with this machine running next to him, pumping like a heart would pump blood. At times he would sit up in bed, even get out of bed and go for a stroll, pulling this machine along with him on a cart. If he is carrying on a conversation, smiling, and discussing things with those at his side, would anyone, even believers in a cardiac definition of death, consider him dead?

This is an unusual case, but it seems clear that Barney Clarke was not dead during this period. What we mean by a somatic- or cardiac-oriented death is that an individual has irreversibly lost the key bodily integrative capacities and that these include cardiac and respiratory functions that normally are controlled by the heart. The fact that these functions are being maintained by some artificial device does not make one dead.

THE PROBLEM OF IRREVERSIBILITY   For an individual to be dead by this definition, the stoppage of bodily integrative function such as circulatory and respiratory function must be *irreversible*. It is very common but very wrong for clinicians and others to refer to someone who has suffered a cardiac arrest and been successfully resuscitated as having been "clinically dead." Being dead means *irreversible* loss of cardiac function. If one suffers a cardiac arrest and then is brought back, that individual was never dead. His or her tissues continued to live. Potentially, we can save that individual. Such individuals have suffered a cardiac arrest and would have died, had we not intervened with CPR (cardiopulmonary resuscitation), but it is incorrect to say that they were ever dead. Consider the recent controversy regarding the procuring of infant hearts for transplantation (Boucek et al., 2008).

CASE 4

Infant Heart Transplant

Although most organ transplants occur after those from whom the organs are taken are pronounced dead based on brain criteria, some organs are taken after patients are pronounced dead using the traditional cardiac-based criteria. Once the heart stops, the patient is pronounced dead and kidneys and other organs are removed. Historically, hearts are not procured in these cases. The reason is that if a heart can be transplanted and restarted, the one from whom the heart was taken cannot have been dead because the heart has not stopped irreversibly.

In 2008 physicians in Denver published an account of their procurement and successful transplant of hearts from three infants who were terminally ill and whose parents had chosen to forgo further life support. In each case, the heart of the infant stopped after life support was withdrawn; death was pronounced based on loss of heart function; hearts were procured and transplanted. No measurements were made that would suggest loss of brain function. In each case the infants receiving these hearts survived with the transplanted hearts functioning appropriately.

Controversy erupted in part because it was question whether the infants from whom the hearts were taken were actually dead. They were not pronounced dead based on loss of brain function. The deaths were based on heart function loss. The controversy centered on whether that function was lost irreversibly. Part of the debate centered on whether the physicians had waited long enough to establish that the hearts would not restart themselves in the chests of the original patients. Part of the controversy was over whether one could claim that the hearts had stopped irreversibly when it, in fact, was successfully restarted (in the chest of the infants receiving the transplants). The issue is of considerable substance since if the infants from whom the hearts were taken were not yet dead (because their hearts had not stopped irreversibly), then the physicians who removed them must have caused the deaths. Homicides must have been committed.

If we understand being dead as signaling a critical change in moral status, it is easy to see why it is important that people must really be dead before their organs are removed. We must follow what is called the "dead donor rule." Life-prolonging organs cannot be removed before death. This helps understand why it is important that we insist that people do not die temporarily only to be brought back to life. If they are dead, many behaviors become appropriate that are totally inappropriate for living people, even unconscious people who are not breathing and temporarily have no heartbeat. We can do things like read the person's will and transfer assets, and, with appropriate permission, remove organs for transplant. The person's spouse becomes a widow. None of that happens with a temporary cardiac arrest. For those who do not believe in reincarnation, we only get one death per individual, at least in this world.

If death is pronounced in such a case and then the patient's cardiac and respiratory function returns, we must say we made a mistake. Death was erroneously pronounced—at least in the eyes of those who hold a somatic- or cardiac-oriented definition of death.

PROBLEMS WITH A SOMATIC DEFINITION OF DEATH   There are some serious problems with a somatic definition of death. For one, there are bad consequences in continuing to use the somatic definition. Thousands and thousands of people around the world are awaiting organs for transplant. In the United States alone there are over 111,000 people on the waiting list for organs as of June 2011. If we wait until somatic integrative functions cease, for the most part those organs are no longer usable in transplants.

It would be nice to be able to get these organs to be used for life-saving transplants. Nevertheless, it is clear we cannot change the definition of death just in order to get wanted organs. In fact, if we wanted to get more organs, we might as well, for example, define all medical students as dead. Then we would get young, healthy organs, rather than waiting for people to have automobile accidents or strokes. It is obvious that we cannot just pick a definition out of thin air simply because it would be useful in saving lives. On the other hand, if there are independent reasons why the somatic-oriented definition seems wrong, then we should begin the task of determining when we believe people lose their full moral status and die.

Many people believe that the somatic- or cardiac-oriented definition of death is no longer appropriate. To claim that people die when their fluids stop flowing is to elevate blood flow to too lofty a place. Likewise, considering people alive simply because they can digest food or excrete bodily wastes seems demeaning. There is more to human life than mere bodily integration. Instead there is another, more complicated explanation of what it means to die.

A Whole-Brain-Oriented Definition of Death

That brings us up to about 1970, when we began talking about what is today sometimes called the **whole-brain-oriented definition of death**. An individual dies, according to this view, when there is irreversible cessation of all functions of the entire brain, including the brain stem (Harvard Medical School, 1968; Task Force on Death and Dying, Institute of Society, Ethics and the Life, 1972; see also The President's Commission for the Study of Ethical Problems in Medicine and Biomedical and Behavioral Research, 1981). The majority of both the 1981 President's Commission and the 2008 report of the President's Council on Bioethics held this view. This is a belief that has traditionally been based on the claim that the essence of humans is their ability to integrate bodily functions, and insofar as we believe that the brain is responsible for that integration, one is dead when and only when the brain irreversibly stops function. The 2008 report of the President's Council emphasized the brain's capacity to make possible human interaction with the surrounding environment. Of course, according to this view one can lose individual functions and still be alive. It is the integrating capacity or interaction with the environment that counts.

Whole-brain death is the current law in most jurisdictions of the world. The exceptions include some Asian countries. Japan only in 1997 adopted a brain-oriented definition of death, limiting it to cases in which organs will be procured for transplant. The resistance of brain-oriented death pronouncement in Asia can be traced mainly to the fact that it does not square well with traditional Buddhist and Shinto beliefs. Also, the very first organs procured for transplant in Japan, back in the late 1960s, may well have been taken from a patient who was not totally dead, so in Japan there is nervousness about procuring organs. The Japanese do not object to procuring organs from a living patient, for instance taking one kidney from a parent to transplant to a child. It is the problem of pronouncing death based on whole-brain death that is the difficulty.[1]

There is one other jurisdiction that still accepts some death pronouncement based on cardiac criteria. That is New Jersey. Policy makers in that state recognize that picking exactly what it means to be dead is not totally a scientific question, that some people could choose one view, some could choose another. In New Jersey, death is based on whole-brain criteria unless the individual had executed a document expressing a religious objection to the use of the whole-brain death concept. This was incorporated primarily to deal with Orthodox Jews, some of whom hold to a cardiac definition. Other groups, including many Native Americans and Japanese, also prefer the more traditional definition.

If his entire brain had been destroyed, as two of the neurologists believed it had been, Yusef Camp would have been dead by whole-brain criteria even though the ventilator was maintaining his heart, respiration, or other bodily integrating functions. Once death has been pronounced, the normal practice would be to stop treatment if it had not already been stopped. Even if one believed that life-supporting treatments should always be provided for living persons (an issue discussed in Chapter 6), many believe there is no reason to provide it if the patient is deceased. Most people hold that treatment can be stopped on one who is dead even against the wishes of the family. Family members have no right, according to this view, to insist that clinicians continue to ventilate a corpse. However, in the case of Yusef Camp, the neurologists could not reach an agreement that the entire brain was destroyed, so they could not use whole-brain death as a way of pronouncing death.

A patient on a ventilator determined to be dead using brain criteria does, of course, make for an unusual corpse. On the ventilator, he is respiring and his heart is beating. But if his whole brain is dead, the law in most jurisdictions says that the patient is deceased.

The Higher-Brain Definition of Death

This brings us to the third definition, sometimes called the **higher-brain-oriented definition**. Suppose a patient were permanently unconscious, with most brain functions gone, but limited reflexes remained in the brain stem. He would not be dead by whole-brain criteria. According to the whole-brain formulation, every last function must be gone. People have begun to say that perhaps there are some brain functions that are not absolutely essential to being considered alive. In that case, we might pronounce somebody dead, if their "higher functions" were permanently lost.

For instance, if the cerebrum is gone, but the brain stem remains so that brain stem reflexes are present, one might, under a higher-brain definition of death, claim somebody is dead. An individual dies, according to this view, when there is an irreversible loss of higher-brain functions.

Defining exactly which functions are critical is controversial. Some have claimed that the critical function is the function of the cerebrum, but it is theoretically possible for some motor functions to remain in the cerebrum even though all sensory function is lost. Most defenders of the higher-brain formulations consider some sensory function to be critical. Some of them simply equate death to an irreversible loss of consciousness. Anybody who is permanently unconscious, according to this newer view, would be considered dead. Since considering someone dead is, in reality, claiming that they have undergone a major change in their moral status, many behaviors appropriate with regard to dead people would become acceptable at this point.

The higher-brain definition of death is not yet legal anyplace in the world. But it is an idea that is debated increasingly. A number of philosophers and neurologists are beginning to endorse this idea. Based on the 2004 Ohio study, it appears that over half (57 percent) of Ohio citizens would consider some people who retain some brain activity to be dead (Siminoff, Burant, and Youngner, 2004). Somebody will eventually propose that it be the legal definition of death. Were it the legal definition of death, Yusef Camp would be dead from the moment he became irreversibly unconscious. Nancy Cruzan and Karen Quinlan (women left in a vegetative state from accidents, whose families led battles for the right to forgo life support) or Terri Schiavo (the Florida woman whose family aired a very public disagreement about withdrawing nutrition) would be dead by this higher-brain definition even though they were legally alive according to the present whole-brain definition.

Definitions and Moral Standing

Almost everyone holds some version of one of these three major definitions of death. They believe that once one has irreversibly lost the critical function—cardiac, whole-brain, or higher-brain—a major moral shift has taken place as well as a biological one. They believe that the individual no longer has the full moral standing that he or she once possessed. Thus, they hold that many behaviors become acceptable that are not appropriate for individuals considered living. They may have lesser moral standing, but full standing no longer exists.

ABORTION

Symmetry Between Definition of Death and Abortion

If calling someone dead is, in fact, a social symbol that we are attributing a major moral status change, the debate over the definition of death is really a great moral debate. Moreover, it may have direct relevance to the even more controversial debate over abortion. Whatever factor signals the end of full moral standing would seem to be relevant to the question of when full moral standing begins. It is possible we can do things before full moral standing is attributed that we will not be able to do later in a human's life. We might, for example, be able to trade off interests, do laboratory manipulations, perhaps even end biological life.

Manipulation of sperm and egg cells are often believed to be less troublesome morally than manipulating a late-term fetus or postnatal infant. It is important to know why that is so. It must be that no matter how we attribute moral status to sperm and egg cells, we view them as having a moral standing that is different from that of the late-term fetus or postnatal infant. If we can identify what is responsible for this perceived shift in moral status, perhaps we can understand better when full moral standing accrues.

Can we use the criterion for end of life as a signal of when full moral standing begins? Some people think this is so. Let us see what the implications of each of the three definitions of death might be for the issue of the moral standing of fetuses. (For a range of well-developed positions on abortion, see Beckwith, 2007; Callahan, 1970; Dworkin, 1994; Feinberg, 1973; Noonan, 1970.)

First, the higher-brain death formulation implies that full moral standing accrues only when the requisite higher functions appear. For many holders of this position that means the capacity for mental function or consciousness. This is late in fetal development, perhaps about twenty-four weeks of gestation. Holders of this view would accept a lesser moral status for fetuses prior to that time, but they would not attribute the same moral status that is assigned to postnatal humans. This concept is probably what underlies the most liberal view on abortion.

Second, the whole-brain death definition implies that full moral standing accrues when capacity for neurological bodily integration or interaction with the environment develops. This is earlier, perhaps in about the eighth to twelfth week. Those who believe that full moral standing accrues at the point at which neurological integrating capacity appears would probably accept abortion up to this point. The exact cutoff would depend on exactly what they understand integration or interaction to mean. They would, thus, be moderates in the abortion debate.

The cardiac definition of death implies that full moral standing accrues when capacity for cardiac function appears. That, in turn, depends on exactly which cardiac function is critical. Full pumping of blood occurs much later, perhaps at a time similar to the occurrence of neurological integrating capacity. Cardiac muscle contraction occurs quite early in fetal development. So do some other somatic integrating functions such as digestion and elimination. If one includes these functions as indicators of life, a more conservative position on abortion is likely.

Each definition of death has a corresponding notion of when full moral standing begins and implications for the moral status of fetuses before that time. None of this implies that a fetus has no moral status before the emergence of the critical function; just as a corpse commands respect even after the critical function ceases, so even liberals on abortion may recognize that early fetuses are not merely meaningless pieces of tissue. There are moral limits on what can be done to a corpse. But those limits are not as constraining as for a being with full moral status. In the case of a dead body, we may transplant organs, do research solely for the benefit of others, perform a respectful autopsy, etc. So, likewise, those who identify a point later in fetal development at which full moral standing begins may still believe fetuses at an earlier stage of development have some intermediate moral status.

Notice that there is no scientific way to choose among these functions to determine which function is critical for maximal standing. This necessarily requires a religious or philosophical judgment. Many in Western society have chosen the whole-brain function as critical in the definition of death. Should they also use that as the critical point in deciding when in fetal development full moral standing accrues? Should those who accept a higher-brain definition of death likewise accept the beginning of these functions as the beginning of full moral standing?

Possible Basis for a Breakdown in the Symmetry

It is striking that none of these positions has anything directly to do with the fixing of the genetic code. None seems to imply full moral standing at the moment of conception. How do conservatives on abortion, those who would oppose all abortion from the beginning, defend their position?

Thus far we have assumed it is the actual capacity to perform some function that is morally critical. That function might be consciousness, neurological integrating capacity, or cardiac function, but it is the *ability to perform* the function that has been taken to be decisive morally. But some people hold that it is the *potential* for these functions that is morally critical. They say that once the genetic code is determined, the eventual development of the critical function is determined. Barring some injury or other untoward event, the capacity will eventually emerge. In death, one loses potential when one loses capacity irreversibility. At the beginning of life, the potential is present long before actual capacity. It is present at conception or soon thereafter. If it is potential for an individual to develop higher-brain, whole-brain, or cardiac function that is morally critical, then full moral standing would arise once that potential has been established.

Liberal critics may claim at this point that potential is present even before conception. The genes are present in sperm and egg, and the potential for combining exists before conception. This claim would appear to give egg and sperm cells full standing, a position almost no one finds plausible. But defenders of the more conservative position claim that what is critical is a potential for these functions occurring *in a unique and individual way*. This occurs only when the genetic code is determined, at least insofar as these functions are determined genetically. If one believes unique potential is what is morally critical to establishing full moral standing, then this moment when the genetic code is fixed becomes critical. A more moderate defender of the potentiality position may recognize that there is at least the possibility for changes in the genetic makeup of an individual for several days after conception (Hellegers, 1970; McCormick, 1991), perhaps up to the point at which twinning can take place. Regardless of when they believe the genetic code is fixed, their ethic is shaped by the belief that full moral standing is contingent on the establishment of the genetically unique individual. This would lead to attributing full moral standing at or near conception no matter which function is critical.

There is one possible exception. If the embryo or fetus has a major defect so that we could determine it could never develop the critical function, then it lacks the potential and would never attain the full moral standing we are discussing. If a fetus is diagnosed as an anencephalic, then holders of a higher-brain view would conclude that the fetus never has the potential for the development of consciousness. Termination of the pregnancy would theoretically be acceptable even for one who was unalterably opposed to abortion of all "living" fetuses. This decision would, of course, require reliance on the higher-brain view and the unique potential view simultaneously. On the other hand, holders of the whole-brain view of which function is critical would still view the anencephalic fetus as having full moral standing. It could not licitly be killed. They would, however, seem logically committed to the view that a fetus so genetically abnormal that had no potential for development of *any* brain function (cerebral or lower) would lack full moral standing. Likewise, the holder of the cardiac or somatic integration view would be committed to the view that a fetus with no potential for any of these functions would lack full moral standing.

HUMAN STEM CELLS

One of the most exciting and controversial developments in recent biology is the emergence of human stem cells as a strategy for medical research and therapy (Gruen, Grabel, and Singer, 2007; *Monitoring Stem Cell Research*, 2008; Monroe, Miller, and Tobis, 2008; National Bioethics Advisory Commission, 1999). Stem cells are undifferentiated cells occurring in multicellular organisms that have the potential to develop into specialized cells of various types. They occur in embryos and in adult organisms and have proven very useful in various kinds of research. They have the potential to be useful in therapy for such diverse conditions as Alzheimer's disease, Parkinson's, strokes, myocardial infarction, and diabetes.

Stem Cells and Moral Standing

Stem cells raise two kinds of moral issues. One arises potentially with both embryonic and adult stem cells. Some people consider that interventions to manipulate the core genetic and cellular structure of humans are too much tampering with nature. They think that generation of replacement cells or organs or conducting research at this level is treading where humans ought not to tread. That issue will be confronted in detail in Chapter 9.

The second issue is more immediate. The production and growth of organisms from stem cells raises issues related to moral standing. That is our focus here. The moral problem arises first in the obtaining of embryonic stem cells. Researchers are also developing the capacity to obtain stem cells from adults (President's Council on Bioethics, 2005), but some insist that embryonic sources are still needed for at least some uses. These come from the inner cell mass of the embryo at the morula or blastocyst stage. This involves destruction of an embryo and thereby the destroying of a human organism that, according to the holders of more conservative views on moral standing, is the immoral killing of a human being. Thus, anyone who is morally opposed to all abortions (even at the earliest stage of embryonic development) would be likely to oppose the destruction of the embryo necessary to obtain embryonic stem cells. Controversy over stem cells is, thus, in part an extension of the controversy over abortion.

A somewhat different issue arises with some efforts to develop stem cells into more differentiated tissues for purposes of research or therapy. The growth of stem cells in some ways produces a new organism, one with the genetic makeup of original stem cell. Whether from adult or a newly formed embryo, some might view the new organism as having enough human characteristics that rights—including potentially the right to life—might be attributed to it.

Stem Cells and Cooperation with Evil

The emergence of stem cells produces a new set of issues for those who would attribute full standing or even high levels of standing less than full to the embryos destroyed in the production of embryonic stem cells. Often the source of these embryos is the in vitro fertilization clinics that intentionally produce human embryos for purposes of treating infertility. Since obtaining the egg cells that are fertilized in these clinics is expensive and burdensome, it is typical that many are procured at the same time. They are fertilized and extras not implanted immediately are stored in case the first efforts fail. This can result in extra embryos not used by the infertile couple that created them.

Assuming that the couple does not wish to donate those extra fertilized eggs for another infertile couple to "adopt" prenatally, these unused embryos would simply be discarded. If, however, they are to be discarded (and thus killed), some might ask whether it would be any more immoral to destroy them in the process of obtaining stem cells and thus creating the possibility that something good would emerge.

Many who would consider the destruction of unwanted embryos immoral would also find the destruction in the process of obtaining stem cells equally unacceptable. Some people, however, might conclude that, as long as the embryos are going to be destroyed anyway, no further wrong is done if they are used as a source of stem cells. Even those who would not themselves be a party to such stem cell procurement may decide that, once the cells have been obtained, it is morally tolerable to make use of cells of a cell line so created.

Critics of the use of embryonic stem cells may argue that the possibility that some good could come from the destruction of the embryos will necessarily add a benign aura to the moral wrong of the original destruction and thus change the moral calculation about obtaining the cells. They may see this as contributing to the condoning of the moral wrong. One who is using the stem cells so obtained is sometimes said to be "cooperating" in the evil of destroying the embryo. There remains some controversy among those who oppose abortion (and thus oppose the destruction of embryos) whether it would be unethical to participate in research on cell lines or in therapies generated by the use of such cell lines. Even if one who is conducting the research had nothing to do with the embryo destruction and was far removed from such activity, there are those who would argue that benefiting down the line would constitute a kind of cooperation that would be unacceptable.

During the administration of George W. Bush, a federal prohibition existed on the use of government funds to create new lines of stem cells although certain cell lines already in existence could still be used in research with federal funding. The Obama administration lifted that ban permitting once again, with certain limits, the production of new cell lines with the use of government funds (Macklin, 2000; Meilaender, 2001).

THE MORAL STATUS OF NON-HUMAN ANIMALS

This discussion of moral standing leads directly into another controversial issue in medicine: the moral status of non-human animals (Council of Europe, 2006; DeGrazia, 2002; Orlans, 1993; Palmer, 2008; Regan and Singer, 1989; Singer, 1975;

Sunstein and Nussbaum, 2004). If clinicians or scientists do research or educational projects using non-human animals, they must confront the question of the moral limits of their use. Radical protestors destroy labs and assault medical personnel fighting over the moral status of non-human animals. In the United States, federal regulations control animal use carefully (U.S. National Institutes of Health, 1985, 1986). The Animal Care and Use Committee must approve animal research just as institutional review boards must approve research on humans.

Do any animals have the "full moral standing" we give to humans, and what would that mean if they did? Western culture has viewed non-human animals as subordinate to humans. They are used for food, medicine, religious ritual, and even sport. This status is reflected in the Judeo-Christian creation story in which humans are to have dominion over the earth and subdue it. This leads to a moral subordination of non-human animals. They are believed to deserve protection from needless suffering, but the interests of humans take precedence. Xenografts (transplantation of organs across species lines) are accepted; in some forms of Judaism they are even imperative. The radical separation between the status of humans and that of animals is seen in the zealous controversy over creation versus evolution. Creationists insist that God has a special relation with humans, who did not merely evolve from other animals.

By contrast, Eastern thought often gives a higher moral status to animals than most Westerners do, and animal suffering causes greater concern. For example, the Hindu doctrine of *ahimsa* (avoidance of suffering) applies to all species. Jains believe no animal should be killed. Their priests actually sweep the ground ahead of them before they walk, to brush insects out of the way.

Western secular thinking has traditionally followed its religious thought in subordinating the moral status of non-human animals, but recently some have taken a different position. Western secular thought is sometimes utilitarian. The focus is exclusively on the amount of good and harm done by an action. Typically, utilitarians treat pain as an evil and pleasure as a good, regardless of the species. An identical kind and quantity of pain counts the same morally regardless of whether it occurs in a human or a non-human. Utilitarians claim that anyone who treats individuals differently solely on the basis of species is guilty of **speciesism** (Singer, 1975). They see it as comparable to racism or sexism or ageism.

Two current views about the moral status of non-humans support concern about animals. One view, the **animal rights perspective** of philosophers such as Tom Regan (1989), holds that sentient animals have a sacredness or right to life just the way humans do. The argument is not driven by concern for consequences. Animals simply have rights, including a right to live. The second position, held by philosophers such as Ray Frey (1989), could be called the "degrees-of-pleasure-and-pain" view. It reflects a **utilitarian perspective**. According to Frey, two animals of different species which experience the same kind and quantity of pain have equal moral claim to be relieved of that pain. But he emphasizes that humans and rats may experience pain differently. Even though a human and a non-human which experienced identical kind and quantity of pain would deserve to be treated equally, if they experience it differently their moral claim would differ.

Frey's view suggests a puzzle: If a chimpanzee has developed mentally to the point that his experiences are richer than those of a severely retarded human, what would justify using the non-human, rather than the human, for research or xenograft or food? How could one defend a priority for the human in such as case? Is species itself a morally defensible dividing line? That is, is speciesism acceptable after all? Or are we prepared to grant to non-human animals which have the functional capacities of severely impaired humans all the moral status we grant humans?

Key Concepts

Cardiac- or Somatic-Oriented Definition of Death   The view that an individual dies when there is irreversible cessation of all cardiac and respiratory functions. If the functions are expanded to include other bodily integrating functions such as digestion, elimination, maintenance of homeostasis, etc., then this is sometimes referred to as the somatic integrating definition of death.

Higher-Brain-Oriented Definition of Death   The view that an individual dies when there is irreversible cessation of all "higher" functions of the brain, often believed to be functions related to consciousness and feelings.

Moral Standing   The status of humans (and other beings) who have moral claims on others or to whom others have duties.

Person (moral definition)   Humans (and other beings) who possess full or maximal moral standing

Person (nonmoral definition)   Humans (and other beings) who possess some critical physical or mental capacity such as self-consciousness, self-awareness, or rationality.

Rights-Based Defense of the Moral Status of Animals   Sentient animals have a sacredness or right to life just the way humans do. The argument is not driven by concern for consequences.

Speciesism   The view in the debate about the moral status of animals that holds that species itself is a morally relevant factor in deciding moral standing, usually in the form of holding that humans, just by being humans, have greater moral standing than non-human animals, even those capable of having similar quantity and quality of experience.

Stem Cells   Cells found in multicellular organisms that are unspecialized and are capable of renewing themselves. Under certain conditions they can become tissue- or organ-specific cells.

Utilitarian Defense of the Moral Status of Animals (the "Degrees of Pleasure and Pain" View)   Animals of different species which experience the same kind and quantity of pleasure or pain have equal moral claim to have the pleasure promoted or to be relieved of that pain.

Whole-Brain-Oriented Definition of Death   The view that an individual dies when there is irreversible cessation of all functions of the entire brain, including the brain stem.

Bibliography

THE DEFINITION OF DEATH

Boucek, Mark M., Christine Mashburn, Susan M. Dunn, Rebecca Frizell, Leah Edwards, Biagio Pietra, and David Campbell, for the Denver Children's Pediatric Heart Transplant Team. "Pediatric Heart Transplantation after Declaration of Cardiocirculatory Death." *New England Journal of Medicine* 359 (2008): 709–714.

Capron, Alexander Morgan. "Death, Definition and Determination of: II. Legal Issues in Pronouncing Death." In *Encyclopedia of Bioethics*, 3rd ed. Ed. Stephen G. Post. New York: Macmillan Reference USA: Thomson/Gale, 2004, pp. 608–615.

Controversies in the Determination of Death: A White Paper by the President's Council on Bioethics. Washington, DC: President's Council on Bioethics, 2008.

Gervais, Karen G. "Death, Definition and Determination of: III. Philosophical and Theological Perspectives." In *Encyclopedia of Bioethics*, 3rd ed. Ed. Stephen G. Post. New York: Macmillan Reference USA: Thomson/Gale, 2004, pp. 615–626.

Harvard Medical School. "A Definition of Irreversible Coma. Report of the Ad Hoc Committee of the Harvard Medical School to Examine the Definition of Brain Death." *Journal of the American Medical Association* 205 (1968): 337–340.

Jonas, Hans. "Against the Stream: Comments on the Definition and Redefinition of Death." *Philosophical Essays: From Ancient Creed to Technological Man.* Englewood Cliffs, NJ: Prentice-Hall, Inc., 1974, pp. 132–140.

Lamb, David. *Death, Brain Death and Ethics.* Albany, NY: The State University of New York Press, 1985.

Law Reform Commission of Canada. *Criteria for the Determination of Death.* Ottawa: Ministry of Supply and Services, 1979.

President's Commission for the Study of Ethical Problems in Medicine and Biomedical and Behavioral Research. *Defining Death: Medical, Legal and Ethical Issues in the Definition of Death.* Washington, DC: U.S. Government Printing Office, 1981.

Shewmon, D. Alan. "The Brain and Somatic Integration: Insights into the Standard Biological Rationale for Equating 'Brain Death' with Death." *Journal of Medicine and Philosophy* 26, No. 5 (2001): 457–478.

Siminoff, Laura A., Chris Burant, and Stuart J. Youngner. "Death and Organ Procurement: Public Beliefs and Attitudes." *Social Science Medicine* 59, No. 11 (December 2004): 2325–2334.

Task Force on Death and Dying, Institute of Society, Ethics and the Life Sciences. "Refinements in Criteria for the Determination of Death: An Appraisal." *Journal of the American Medical Association* 221 (1972): 48–53.

Veatch, Robert M. "The Whole-Brain-Oriented Concept of Death: An Outmoded Philosophical Formulation." *Journal of Thanatology* 3 (1975): 13–30.

Youngner, Stuart J., Robert M. Arnold, and Renie Schapiro, eds. *The Definition of Death: Contemporary Controversies.* Baltimore, MD: Johns Hopkins University Press, 1999.

ABORTION

Beckwith, Francis J. *Defending Life: A Moral and Legal Case Against Abortion Choice.* Cambridge/New York: Cambridge University Press, 2007.

Callahan, Daniel. *Abortion: Law, Choice and Morality.* New York: Macmillan, 1970.

Dworkin, Ronald. *Life's Dominion: An Argument about Abortion, Euthanasia, and Individual Freedom.* New York: Vintage Books, 1994.

Feinberg, Joel, ed. *The Problem of Abortion.* Belmont, CA: Wadsworth, 1973.

Hellegers, A. "Fetal Development." *Theological Studies* 31 (March 1970): 3–9.

McCormick, Richard A. "Who or What Is the Preembryo?" *Kennedy Institute of Ethics Journal* 1 (1991): 1–15, esp. 4, 9, 11–12.

Noonan, John T. *The Morality of Abortion: Legal and Historical Perspectives*. Cambridge, MA: Harvard University Press, 1970.

STEM CELLS

Gruen, Lori, Laura Grabel, and Peter Singer, eds. *Stem Cell Research: The Ethical Issues*. Malden, MA: Blackwell Publishing, 2007.

Macklin, Ruth. "Ethics, Politics, and Human Embryo Stem Cell Research." *Women's Health Issues* 10, No. 3 (May–June 2000): 111–115.

Meilaender, Gilbert. "The Point of a Ban. Or, How to Think about Stem Cell Research." *Hastings Center Report* 31, No. 1 (January–February 2001): 9–16.

Monitoring Stem Cell Research: A Report of the President's Council on Bioethics. Washington, DC: President's Council on Bioethics, 2008.

Monroe, Kristin Renwick, Ronald B. Miller, and Jerome Tobis, eds. In *Fundamentals of the Stem Cell Debate: The Scientific, Religious, Ethical, and Political Issues*. Berkeley, CA: University of California Press, 2008.

National Bioethics Advisory Commission. *Ethical Issues in Human Stem Cell Research Volume I: Report and Recommendations of the National Bioethics Advisory Commission*. Rockville, MD: National Bioethics Advisory Commission, September 1999.

MORAL STANDING OF NON-HUMAN ANIMALS

Council of Europe. *Animal Welfare*. Strasbourg: Council of Europe, 2006.

DeGrazia, David. *Animal Rights: A Very Short Introduction*. Oxford/New York: Oxford University Press, 2002.

Frey, R. G. "The Case Against Animal Rights." In *Animal Rights and Human Obligations*, 2nd ed. Ed. Tom Regan and Peter Singer. Englewood Cliffs, NJ: Prentice Hall, 1989, pp. 115–118.

National Research Council (United States). Commission on Life Sciences. Institute of Animal Resources. *Guide for the Care and Use of Laboratory Animals*. Washington, DC: National Academy Press, 1996.

Orlans, F. Barbara. *In the Name of Science: Issues in Responsible Animal Experimentation*. New York: Oxford University Press, 1993.

Orlans, F. Barbara, et al. *The Human Use of Animals: Case Studies in Ethical Choice*. New York: Oxford University Press, 1998.

Palmer, Clare, ed. *Animal Rights*. Aldershot, Hampshire, England/Burlington, VT: Ashgate, 2008.

President's Council on Bioethics. *Alternative Sources of Human Pluripotent Stem Cells*. Washington, DC: President's Council on Bioethics, 2005.

Regan, Tom, and Peter Singer, eds. *Animal Rights and Human Obligations*, 2nd ed. Englewood Cliffs, NJ: Prentice Hall, 1989.

Regan, Tom. "The Case for Animal Rights." In *Animal Rights and Human Obligation*, 2nd ed. Ed. Tom Regan and Peter Singer. Englewood Cliffs, NJ: Prentice Hall, 1989, pp. 105–114.

Singer, Peter. *Animal Liberation: A New Ethics For Our Treatment of Animals*. New York: Avon Books, 1975.

Sunstein, Cass R., and Martha C. Nussbaum, eds. *Animal Rights: Current Debates and New Directions*. Oxford/New York: Oxford University Press, 2004.

U.S. National Institutes of Health. "Laboratory Animal Welfare: Public Health Service Policy on Humane Care and Use of Laboratory Animals by Awardee Institutions; Notice." *Federal Register* 50, No. 90 (May 9, 1985): 19584–19585.

U.S. National Institutes of Health. Office for Protection from Research Risks. *Public Health Service Policy on Humane Care and Use of Laboratory Animals*. Bethesda, MD: Office for Protection from Research Risks, September 28, 1986.

U.S. President's Council on Bioethics. *Controversies in the Determination of Death: A White Paper by the President's Council on Bioethics*. Washington, DC: President's Council on Bioethics, 2008.

Notes

1. Denmark has an ongoing debate. It has been the primary site of controversy on this issue in Europe. In Denmark it is legal to pronounce death by brain criteria, but some scholars and policy makers there are not willing to accept that conclusion.

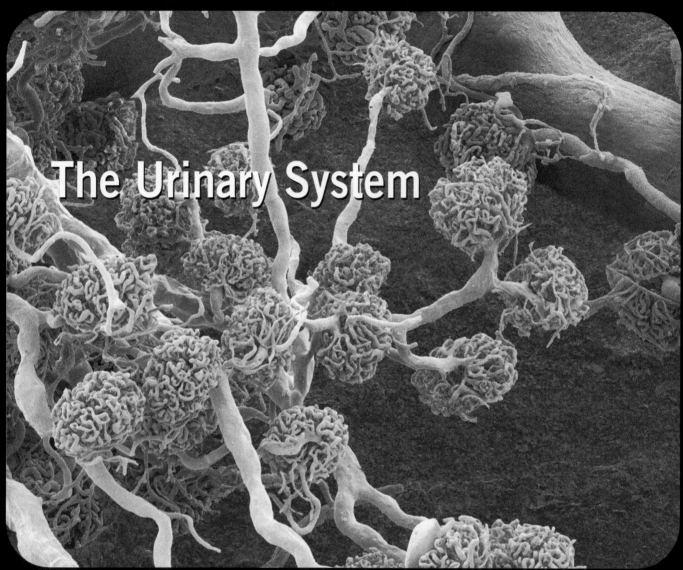

The Urinary System

Steve Gschmeissner/Photo Researchers

SEM of kidney glomeruli (red) and the blood vessels that supply them. The glomerular capsule and the nephron tubules have been removed.

How Should We Allocate Scarce Kidneys?

Over 60% of all organs transplanted every year are kidneys. For years now, a serious imbalance has been developing between the numbers of kidneys available for transplant and the number of patients needing them (see graph). Where do kidneys for transplant come from, and who decides who gets a kidney (or any other transplantable organ, for that matter) when one becomes available?

About 40% of all donated kidneys come from living donors. Patient and donor must have the same blood type and be tested for six key tissue antigens that determine the closeness of the

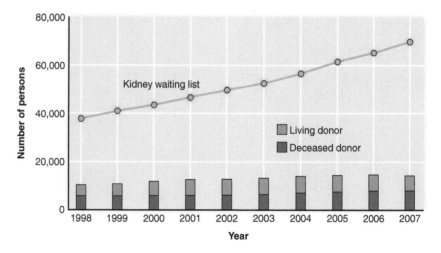

immunological match. Living donors are usually close relatives, but even among close relatives the chances of a perfect match are not all that good. Matches between unrelated donors are rare. *The responsibility for finding a living donor rests with the patient.* There is no national registry of living unrelated potential donors.

If a patient cannot find his/her own living donor or if he/she needs an organ that cannot be taken from a living donor, such as a heart or a pancreas, the only source is a deceased person (a cadaver). Organs may be harvested from a cadaver only when permission has been granted by the deceased or by the deceased's relatives. Persons who wish to donate their organs after death can make their wishes known by signing and carrying a uniform donor card available through most state motor vehicle departments or on the Web. Fewer than half of all adults have signed an organ donor card.

How Are Cadaver Kidneys Currently Allocated?

Cadaver kidneys are allocated to patients according to federal rules established by the Department of Health and Human Services (DHHS). Under the rules, patients who need a cadaveric kidney place themselves on the transplant list of one of 11 regional Organ Procurement Organizations (OPO), linked together by the United Network for Organ Sharing (UNOS), a national private nonprofit corporation. UNOS maintains the national waiting lists of potential transplant recipients. When a cadaver kidney becomes available in a particular region it is tested for blood type and the six antigens. Perfect matches—the same blood type and the same six antigens—are so rare that a patient anywhere in the country has first priority for a perfectly matched kidney.

For all partial matches, the kidney is first made available to all patients in the region of the OPO that procured the organ. Only if none of the patients in that region is considered suitable is the kidney made

James A. Finley/AP Worldwide Photos

Madolena (in yellow) chose to give one of her kidneys to a total stranger, Tracy (center). Here they meet for the first time.

available (by UNOS) to patients in other OPOs. A patient's income is not supposed to be a consideration, but people who are willing to pay for the transplant themselves can put themselves on the transplant lists of several OPOs simultaneously (insurance generally pays for a transplant only in the patient's primary OPO).

Critics charge that the current system is unfair because organs do not always go to the sickest patients, who need them the most. The current system may also discriminate against minorities and the poor because they live in regions that have lower rates of organ donation.

Developments to Watch

Currently it is against the law to sell a kidney—they can only be donated. Studies show that only about 50% of families of a deceased potential donor give their consent even when asked. To increase this number, the American Medical Association suggests that families who donate cadaveric kidneys from a loved one should be "compensated" in some way, but so far it hasn't happened. The DHHS is considering proposals to compensate living kidney donors as well.

At least 21 countries have adopted "presumed consent" laws. Under presumed consent, organs are presumed to be available for donation unless the donor (or family) explicitly states otherwise. Presumed

consent laws have dramatically increased donations in countries that have adopted them. In the United States, however, presumed consent laws have not gained widespread acceptance, because they can be viewed as a subtle form of government coercion or religious discrimination.

Some patients are finding their own unrelated living donors by turning to the Internet. The first commercial Web site to match living organ donor volunteers with potential patients was MatchingDonors.com. Patients who need an organ make an appeal on the site, and potential donors read through them and choose a patient to help, provided the immunological match is good. Donors receive no financial rewards for their donation, but perhaps money can't buy the ultimate gift. As one donor put it, "I wanted to do something nice for somebody." Another site, called LifeSharers, is for people who agree to make their organs available first to others who have also agreed to donate their organs when they die, in exchange for the chance of receiving an organ from the network should they themselves need one.

Organ gifting via the Internet is not such a good idea, according to some ethicists. They point out that when matches are made on sites such as MatchingDonors.com, organs are more likely to go to patients with the best story or the best photo, not the sickest patients.

At least five states (Kentucky, Louisiana, Oklahoma, South Carolina, and Wisconsin) have passed laws mandating that organs donated in their states must be offered first to in-state patients. Whether these laws will stand up under challenge is an open question. The battle for scarce organs continues.

Questions to consider

1 How do you think we should allocate cadaveric kidneys and other organs? What improvements, if any, would you suggest to the present system?

2 Would you be willing to donate your kidneys or other organs after death? Have you completed a donor card?

3 Should the government set up a national registry to match living donors with unrelated patients? Why or why not?

The facts...

- There are not enough donated cadaveric kidneys to meet the growing need for kidney transplants.
- The responsibility for finding a living donor rests with the patient.
- Under current federal allocation rules, where you live may affect your chances of receiving a cadaveric kidney.
- Some patients are using Web sites to locate unrelated living donors.

The Skeletal System

GustoImages/SPL/Photo Researchers

A colored X-ray of a foot on tiptoe.

A Black Market in Human Bones?

Alistair Cooke, famed host of the PBS series *Masterpiece Theatre,* died in 2004 at the age of 95. His body lay in a New York City funeral parlor for a few days awaiting cremation. But before Cooke's body was cremated, it was secretly carved up in a back room and his bones were removed. Authorities allege that his bones were then sold for a substantial profit, to be transplanted into patients in desperate need of tissue grafts.

Cooke's family, who had not given permission for his body parts to be donated, knew nothing of this until police contacted them after the funeral. Understandably, they were appalled. But there is an even more horrifying side to this story: Cooke died of lung cancer that had spread to his bones. Could his deadly cancer have been transmitted to the people who received his bone tissue? Its unlikely since bone products generally are sterilized (see below), but the answer may not be known for decades.

Recycling Body Parts: A Legitimate Industry

The processing of tissues taken from human corpses into products that can be transplanted into other people is a legitimate industry that serves urgent medical needs. The industry has evolved

Corbis

Alistair Cooke, long-time host of *Masterpiece Theatre.* Cooke's body was subjected to secret, illegal bone harvesting after he died.

Donated bones are cleaned, sterilized, and shaped into bone products.

AP Photo/Noah Berger

over the past several decades as harvesting and transplantation techniques have improved. Bones are used to repair fractures and replace cancerous bone. Bone pins and powdered bone are used in dental surgery; bone paste plugs holes. Tendons and ligaments are used to repair joints and tissues damaged by sports injuries, transplanted vertebrae relieve back pain, and veins and heart valves are used in heart surgeries. The bones, tendons, veins, and heart valves from just one corpse can be worth over $200,000 to surgeons, hospitals, and recipients.

Under federal law it is illegal to sell human body parts for a profit—they can only be donated, either by the patient while he or she is still alive or by the family after death. Several hundred licensed nonprofit tissue banks in the United States receive donated tissues and test them for infectious diseases such as HIV, syphilis, and the viruses that cause hepatitis (inflammation of the liver). To reduce the chances of tissue products transmitting disease, authorities impose strict guidelines that specify what types of tissues may be harvested, from whom they may be harvested, and how they must be processed. For instance, to prevent any risk of transmitting cancer, federal guidelines prohibit the use of bones from cancer patients for tissue implants.

After donation, bone tissue is shaped into usable forms, such as pins, plates, and powders. The final products are sterilized and shipped to hospitals and surgeons all over the country, where they are used in more than 600,000 surgical procedures every year. The patient pays all fees incurred in the handling, processing, testing, and shipping of the products, but the tissue banks themselves do not make a profit.

Illegal Body Parts Enter the Supply Chain

In the Alistair Cooke case, prosecutors alleged that Michael Mastromarino, an oral surgeon who had lost his license, arranged for a Brooklyn funeral parlor to deliver bodies to a secret operating room. There, Mastromarino and his accomplices removed body parts before the bodies were buried or cremated. Authorities say that the men paid the funeral parlor up to $1,000 per body and then sold the harvested tissues for up to $7,000 per body to a legitimate but unsuspecting tissue-processing company.

In some cases Mastromarino and his accomplices falsified records indicating the deceased's age and cause of death. Mr. Cooke died of cancer at the age of 95, but his records were falsified to indicate that he died at age 85 of a heart attack. They also allegedly looted body parts from a 43-year-old woman who had died of ovarian cancer; they then forged a signature on a consent form and listed the cause of death as a head injury. When investigators examined the corpse of one grandmother, they found that her leg bones had been removed and replaced with PVC pipes. Prosecutors eventually identified over a thousand corpses from which body parts were taken without permission between 2001 and 2005.

In 2008 Mr. Mastromarino plead guilty in a plea bargain that could reduce his jail time in exchange for providing information about others who were involved. He is expected to spend at least 18 years in

prison. An accomplice and seven funeral home directors received lesser sentences.

Just as the Alistair Cooke case is not the first such incident, it is not likely to be the last. In 1999 the University of California at Irvine discovered that the director of its Willed Body Program was selling human spines to a Phoenix hospital for $5,000 apiece. And in 2008 the director of UCLA's Willed Body Program was sentenced to 4 years in prison for selling more than a million dollars worth of body parts. Regulators say that abuses such as these are most likely to occur when relatively poorly paid directors (including funeral home directors) have access to valuable body parts and when oversight is lax. UC Irvine and UCLA have both tightened their oversight procedures as a result of the scandals.

Only 22,000 cadavers are donated annually for body parts—not enough to supply the growing demand for human body parts and tissues. Done properly, the donation of a single cadaver to a nonprofit tissue-processing company can benefit several dozen patients. Patients should only have to pay the legitimate costs associated with the body parts processing industry—not the added fees paid to traffickers in illegal body parts. Safeguards need to be put in place to prevent abuses so that we can be assured of the legitimacy and the safety of the supply of human body parts.

Kevin Beebe/Newscom

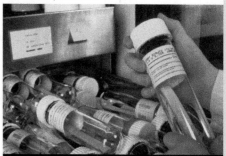
Human bones and bone products ready for shipment to hospitals.

Questions to consider

1 Do you approve of human bones being harvested from cadavers for processing into bone-based products for patients, provided the bones are legally obtained?

2 What steps do you think should be taken to curb abuses in the human body parts industry?

The facts...

- It is illegal to buy or sell human body parts for a profit. Patients or their families can donate body parts only to nonprofit tissue banks.

- Legitimately donated tissues are tested, sterilized, processed, and transplanted into patients who urgently need them.

- Only 22,000 cadavers are donated annually for body parts—not enough to meet the growing legitimate demand for human tissues and tissue products.

- The supply/demand imbalance may be contributing to a black market in body parts harvested illegally from cadavers.

Fatal Flaw

Timothy Gower

A 1983 graduate of the University of Massachusetts at Amherst, Timothy Gower worked as a feature writer and assistant editor at the Boston Phoenix *from 1990 to 1994, and has written for publications as varied as the* New York Times, Reader's Digest, Esquire, *and* Health. *He has published several books, including* Staying at the Top of Your Game: A Man's Guide to Peak Performance *(1999),* A Doctor's Guide to Herbs and Supplements *(with Robert DiPaola, 2001),* The Diabetic Body: An Owner's Manual *(2007), and* The Sugar Fix: The High-Fructose Fallout that Is Making You Fat and Sick *(with Richard Johnson, 2008). At present, Gower is a freelance writer specializing in the areas of health, psychiatry, nutrition, and medicine. In this selection he tackles one of the most controversial issues in medical ethics today, the definition of death. Media interest in the issue normally revolves around questions of whether or not to "pull the plug" on a patient in a persistent vegetative state, but, as Gower explains here, an even more compelling concern involves harvesting organs for transplant. Beyond the question of how to determine death, some doctors are also considering whether or not organs may be harvested from patients in irreversible comas.*

1 When is a person dead—or dead enough?

The question has long influenced decisions about when it's appropriate to end medical treatment for people who are hopelessly ill. However, a quieter debate has simmered for years about how the concept of death informs the practice of organ

---

Reprinted from the *Boston Globe*, March 9, 2008, by permission of the author.

transplantation. Transplant surgeons rely on strict definitions of death to reassure would-be donors. Wary of the macabre suggestion that they are willing to exploit the dying for their organs, surgeons abide by a code known as the "dead donor rule," which forbids removing body parts from the living.

Yet a few outspoken medical ethicists say the dead donor rule is broken all the time—and, perhaps even more surprising, that the rule itself should be abandoned. The dead donor rule, they argue, prevents some terminally ill patients from donating organs, even if they want to. And, they say, it has become clear that doctors will never be able to devise a coherent definition of death. Even the concept of "brain death," the diagnosis of most deceased organ donors, falls apart on closer examination. Why not, they ask, simply admit that some people donate vital organs when they are, in some important way, still alive?

"It's completely ethical to remove organs from patients we diagnose as brain dead," says Dr. Robert Truog, director of clinical ethics at Harvard Medical School and a physician at Children's Hospital Boston. "It's just ethical for reasons other than that we think they're dead, because I don't think they are."

5   Truog is one of a handful of vocal critics who believe the medical community is misleading the public—and deluding itself—with an arbitrary definition of death. The debate, which is being fought largely in academic journals, has important implications for the modern enterprise of transplantation, which prolonged the life of more than 28,000 Americans last year. Truog and other critics believe that changing the rules—and the bright-line concept of death that underlies them—could mean saving more of the 6,500 Americans who die every year waiting for an organ.

Although Truog says many doctors have problems with the concept of brain death, it is an established medical and legal standard. And its numerous defenders worry that allowing organs to be taken from people who haven't completely died, or even discussing it, would greatly compromise the public's confidence in organ transplantation.

"There is no controversy about brain death," says Dr. Eelco Wijdicks, a Mayo Clinic neurologist and a leading authority on the topic. Wijdicks says the concept is widely embraced by neurosurgeons and neurologists. Claims by "brain death rejecters" that the concept is flawed, he says, don't jibe with his clinical experience. "What they describe is not what we see."

The current debate about transplantation ethics has been intensified by the growing use of a technique for obtaining organs called donation after cardiac death (DCD), in which surgeons start harvesting soon after a patient's heart stops—too soon for some people, who worry that potential donors may gain the impression that surgeons are overly eager to take their flesh. That impression was reinforced by recent news stories about an attempted DCD procedure at a hospital in California; a prosecutor there charges that a surgeon ordered nurses to give morphine and other drugs to hasten a patient's death.

This debate exposes a jarring collision: On the one hand, there is the view that life and death are clear categories; on the other, there is the view that death, like life, is a process. Common sense—and the transplant community—suggest that death is a clear category. Truog and other critics suggest that this is to ignore reality.

10   "They think, 'We can't remove these organs unless we decide that   10
you're dead,'" says Truog, "so the project becomes gerrymandering the criteria we use to call people dead."

Modern medical advances have blurred the line between life and death. In the past, most people, including doctors, thought death occurred when the heart stopped and blood ceased to flow. (At least in a biological sense; most major religions define death as the departure of the soul from the body.) However, by the mid-20th century, new medical devices such as the mechanical ventilator allowed doctors to keep the hearts and lungs working in severely brain-damaged people who in an earlier era would have died. In 1959, two French physicians coined the phrase coma dépassé, or "irreversible coma," to describe these patients' ambiguous condition.

Doctors in the United States eventually came up with another name: brain death. In 1968, a group of physicians, ethicists, and other experts at Harvard Medical School published guidelines for diagnosing what they called "a new criterion of death." Because of this influential report, a patient can be declared dead in the United States, and most countries, if their blood circulation and breathing have permanently stopped or they have suffered total and irreversible brain damage.

Most organs donated from the deceased come from people who have been diagnosed as brain dead. Organs remain viable for only about an hour or two after a person's last heartbeat. Brain dead patients are ideal candidates for organ donation, then, because they are kept on ventilators, which means their heart and lungs continue to work, ensuring that a steady flow of oxygen-rich blood keeps their organs healthy. Surgeons remove the donor's organs, then shut off the ventilator. The patient's heart eventually stops.

Yet a small but vocal minority in the medical community has always insisted that some brain dead patients may not be dead. For instance, one study documented some kind of brain activity in up to 20 percent of people declared brain dead, suggesting to some critics that doctors sometimes misdiagnose the condition. Although some neurologists contend the claim, University of Wisconsin medical ethicist Dr. Norman Fost points to research showing that many "brain dead" patients have a functioning hypothalamus, a structure at the base of the brain that governs certain bodily functions, such as blood pressure and appetite.

15   "We have been taking organs out of those patients by the thousands," says Fost, "and they are not brain dead."   15

Others point to the unsettling fact that the brain dead look alive—their hearts beat, lungs function (albeit with the aid of a respirator), and skin retains a pink hue. Brain dead women have even given birth.

"There is nobody in the world of philosophy and bioethics who thinks brain death is a coherent concept," says Truog.

It's important to point out that the dead donor rule does not say a patient must be brain dead—just dead. To help meet the urgent need for donors, many transplant centers now recover organs from people who have suffered cardiac death using the DCD procedure. In 1993 there were 43 DCD procedures in the United States; there were 670 in the first nine months of 2007.

The typical DCD donor is a patient who is severely brain damaged, but not brain dead, and surviving on a ventilator. With his or her family's consent, doctors remove the ventilator and wait for the heart to stop. If that occurs within an hour or two (hospitals use different standards), the patient's organs are still viable. Death is declared and surgery starts quickly, within two minutes at some transplant centers.

20   It's safe to assume a person is dead two minutes after the last heartbeat, says Dr. Michael DeVita, a University of Pittsburgh transplant surgeon and an authority on DCD. That's because there are no   20

recorded cases of hearts spontaneously restarting after 65 seconds, he says. "Death can be determined when circulation will not resume on its own."

Skeptics point out, though, that countless people whose hearts have stopped have been resuscitated with defibrillators past the two-minute mark. Were they dead? Some skeptics think the definition of cardiac death is no more satisfying than brain death for determining when life ends.

"The DCD protocol pretends that patients are dead at the time organs are taken out," says Fost. "They're not."

Yet Fost does not oppose the DCD procedure. He believes that consenting people should be able to stipulate that their organs can be removed before they die, as long as they are terminally ill. This simply respects the individual's right to make decisions about their own medical care. If that includes having your pancreas plucked out before dying, so be it. The idea doesn't sound so nutty to some people, he insists. He cites a 2004 survey by Case Western Reserve University ethicist Stuart Youngner and colleagues of 1,300 adults in Ohio, in which almost half of the respondents said they would support taking organs from someone who was alive but in an irreversible coma.

Many doctors say that eliminating the dead donor rule will likely never happen, a notion its opponents acknowledge. Even if the public accepted the idea, lawmakers would never support statutes protecting doctors from charges of homicide—necessary, since taking organs from the dying would obviously be the cause of death if a heart was removed (a "lethal donation," in Truog's words).

25   The dead donor rule helps to uphold public confidence in organ   25 transplantation, which is "somewhat shaky," says Dr. James L. Bernat, a Dartmouth Medical School neurologist. And breaking the taboo, he worries, could eventually lead ethically challenged doctors to take organs without patient consent.

Another opponent of abandoning the dead donor rule, Georgetown University ethicist Robert Veatch, proposes an alternative that would create a new source of organs: Give people the choice of being declared dead if they enter a persistent vegetative state or otherwise suffer loss of consciousness forever, but still have some brain function. "There would be nothing lost and a lot gained—respect for individual judgment," says Veatch.

Yet this debate will likely be moot in 20 years or so, says Truog. By then, he predicts, genetically modified animals—probably pigs—will provide all the organs we need, eliminating the need for human harvesting. If that happens, perhaps the need to define death in clinical terms will seem that much less urgent, while references to taking organs from humans will likely disappear from medical texts. "The concept," Truog wrote recently, "will have died a natural death of its own."

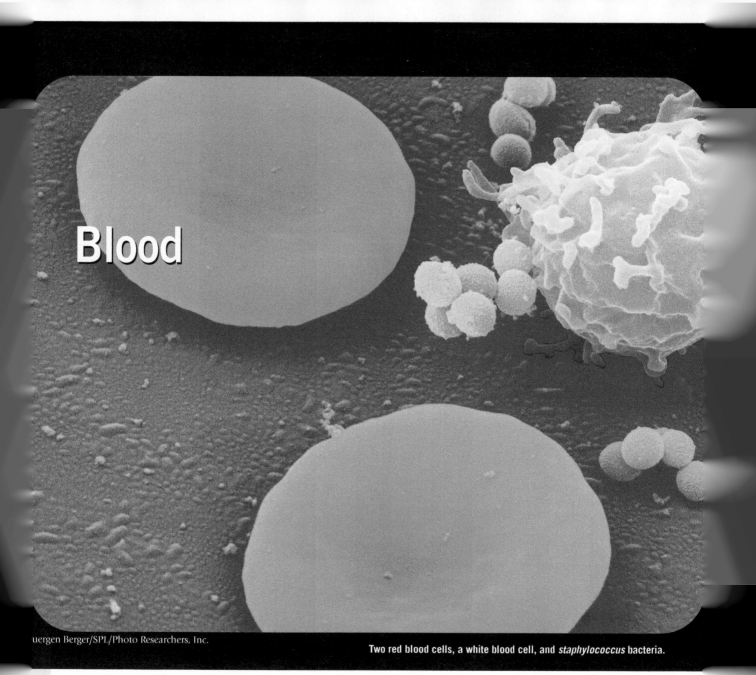

Blood

Two red blood cells, a white blood cell, and *staphylococcus* bacteria.

Current Issue

Should You Bank Your Baby's Cord Blood?

When she was 15 and a sophomore in high school, Jaclyn Albanese was diagnosed with acute leukemia—a type of cancer of stem cells in bone marrow. The usual treatment is chemotherapy and radiation to kill the cancer cells (and normal stem cells), and then a bone marrow transplant to repopulate the bone marrow with stem cells. Traditionally these stem cells have come from bone marrow donated by a family member or an unrelated volunteer whose marrow is compatible. Compatibility is crucial because, as you will learn in this chapter, the body's immune cells recognize and attack foreign cells. Jaclyn had hoped to get a bone marrow transplant from one of her relatives, but none of them was a close enough match. Fortunately for Jaclyn, she found compatible units of cord blood from an unrelated donor. They saved her life. But, if her parents had banked the cord blood from her delivery when she was born, she wouldn't have needed to search for donors at all.

What Is Cord Blood?

During pregnancy, the fetus is cushioned by a temporary organ called the placenta and connected to its mother by the umbilical cord. Blood vessels in the umbilical cord and placenta filter out toxic

Jaclyn Albanese

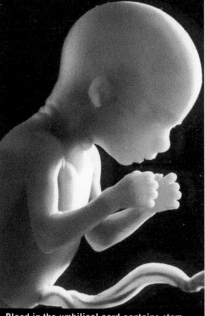

Blood in the umbilical cord contains stem cells similar to those found in bone marrow.

substances, deliver nutrients from the mother, and remove waste products from the fetus. After the baby is delivered, the mother's body expels the placenta and umbilical cord. A health professional cuts the cord, and the baby's circulatory system begins to function on its own.

Until recently, the placenta and cord were discarded after birth. However, these structures still contain about 50 ml of cord blood. In addition to containing the usual components of blood, cord blood is rich in stem cells from the fetus that are still relatively immature. These stem cells can be coaxed to divide repeatedly to produce immature blood cells, which in turn develop into platelets, red cells, and white cells.

Bone Marrow, Cord Blood, and Compatibility Issues

A good bone marrow transplant match between a donor and a patient involves three key antigens known as HLA-A, HLA-B, and HLA-DR, each of which comes in two forms. The ideal match would be for the patient to have the same six forms as the donor (a 6/6 match). Good matches between unrelated donors are rare—siblings of the same parents match only 25% of the time, and only about 10% of all patients who need a bone marrow transplant are able to find a compatible match from among unrelated donors.

This is why cord blood has become such a precious commodity. The immune cells in cord blood are less mature than those in bone marrow, so cord blood transplants are less likely to cause transfusion reactions, and even when reactions do occur, they tend to be less severe. As a result, the match between donor and recipient does not need to be a perfect 6/6—matches of 5/6 or even 4/6 are sufficient. This opens a much wider field of possibilities. Jaclyn Albanese could not find a single compatible bone marrow donor, but she was able to locate two units of compatible cord blood. She had a cord blood transplant in 1999 just prior to her junior year in high school, and today she is a college graduate. Jaclyn is one of approximately 6,000 patients who have benefited from cord blood transplants to date.

Banking Privately or Publicly

Should you bank your baby's cord blood privately, or donate it to a public cord blood bank?

Private blood banks say that banking your baby's cord blood privately is like taking out a medical insurance policy. They argue that you might want to use your baby's cord blood stem cells to treat a future disease (such as leukemia) in your child or a close family member. By banking your baby's cord blood, you ensure that your child always has access to the "perfect match"—his or her own stem cells. They also point out that scientists are working on stem-cell therapies for a variety of other conditions such as diabetes and heart disease. The implication is that in 30 or 40 years, by the time your newborn is at greater risk of developing these chronic ailments, he or she may be able to use these stem cells for treatments as yet undreamed of. So far they have convinced over 20,000 families to have their baby's cord blood collected, processed, tested, and stored, at an average cost of $1,700 plus an annual storage fee of about $125.

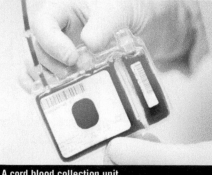

A cord blood collection unit.

Proponents of public blood banking argue that the likelihood of a baby born to a healthy family ever needing his or her stem cells range from one in 10,000 to one in 200,000. Is such an unlikely event worth hoarding your baby's blood? If you and your family are healthy, you might want to consider helping others by donating your child's cord blood to a public cord blood bank. To support public donations, in 2005 the federal government authorized $79 million in federal funds to collect and store cord blood from ethnically diverse donors. As a result, the National Marrow Donor Program now lists a national inventory of over 90,000 cord blood units. An inventory of 140,000 units would give all Americans an 80–90% chance of finding at least a 5/6 antigen match.

Jaclyn Albanese's parents did not have the choice of banking her cord blood privately when she was born—the technology didn't exist back then. Fortunately, she was able to rely on the generosity of others who donated their baby's cord blood to a public cord blood bank.

Questions to consider

1 Do you agree with the federal government's decision to allocate $79 million (about 40 cents per adult) for a public cord blood collection and storage network?

2 When (or if) you have a child, what will you do with its cord blood? Explain your decision.

The facts...

- Cord blood—blood remaining in a newborn baby's placenta and umbilical cord—is rich in stem cells similar to those found in bone marrow.
- Cord blood can benefit many patients who cannot find a suitable bone marrow donor.
- Private cord blood banks urge prospective parents to bank their baby's cord blood solely for their own child's future use.
- The federal government has established a public cord blood network for all Americans.

Du Cane Medical Imaging Ltd./Photo Researchers, Inc.

Colorized chest X-ray showing a cancerous lung tumor (red/yellow).

Cancer: Uncontrolled Cell Division and Differentiation

Voluntary Breast and Ovary Removal

René Syler, former anchorwoman of CBS's The Early Show, faced a difficult decision. Both her mother and her father had suffered from breast cancer (breast cancer is rare in males). She had had numerous mammograms and several biopsies of suspected cancer tissue. Although she did not yet have cancer, it felt as if she were just waiting for it to happen. Her breasts were shrunken and scarred from the biopsies, and she was scared and just tired of it all. So René made a decision to take control of her own health. She said, "Instead of asking, 'Is this the year I get breast cancer?' I had to say,

'I will not get breast cancer this year. Or ever.'"[1] On January 2, 2007 she had both breasts removed.

Could You Do It?

Would you choose to have your breasts and ovaries removed surgically (called prophylactic mastectomy and oophorectomy) in order to avoid breast and ovarian cancer? Women can now make that decision while they are still in good health, thanks to our increased

---

[1]René Syler. Defending My Life. *O, The Oprah Magazine*, April 15, 2007.

understanding of the causes of cancer and our ability to test for some of the known risk factors. It is now known that mutations in at least two genes, called BRCA1 (short for breast cancer 1) and BRCA2, are strongly associated with breast and ovarian cancer. In their normal forms these two genes function to suppress cell growth; only the mutated forms increase the risk of cancer.

Mutated forms of BRCA genes are relatively rare—only 0.5% of all women have a mutated form—but for those who do, the risk of cancer goes up dramatically. For all women the lifetime risk of developing breast cancer is 12%, according to the

René Syler, former anchorwoman of CBS's. The Early Show, had both breasts removed and reconstructed in 2007 as a preemptive strike against breast cancer.

National Cancer Institute. For women with a mutated BRCA gene the risk of breast cancer is about 60%, or five times as high. For ovarian cancer the lifetime risk is 1.4% for all women versus 15-40% for women with a mutated BRCA gene.

Testing for mutated forms of BRCA1 and BRCA2 genes is relatively easy, requiring only a blood sample. That means that women can find out whether they are at high risk for breast and ovarian cancers long before the cancers might actually develop.

Should you be tested for the BRCA genes just as a precaution? That depends on whether you would really want to know the answer, and what (if anything) you

would choose to do if you did know you had the BRCA genes. If you are convinced that you could never have your breasts and ovaries removed while you are still healthy, then perhaps you would be better off not knowing. Your decision might also be influenced by whether or not you have other risk factors. Although fewer than 0.5% of all women have a mutated BRCA gene, your chances of having a mutated gene go up five-to tenfold if you have a family history of women who developed breast or ovarian cancer. In fact, both of the BRCA genes can be inherited from either of your parents (in men, the BRCA genes are associated with slightly increased risks of breast and prostate cancer).

If you inherited a mutated BRCA gene, couldn't you just wait to see if cancer ever developed in a breast or ovary, and then (and only then) have it removed? After all, if you're still of reproductive age you may want to have children. The problem is that ovarian cancer is particularly deadly. There is no easy screening test for ovarian cancer and there are generally no symptoms in the early stages, so it may not be diagnosed until it is already in an advanced stage. The five-year survival rate after a diagnosis of ovarian cancer is still under 40%.

After oophorectomy, the risk of developing ovarian cancer essentially disappears. The risk of developing breast cancer after mastectomy drops by 90% if you have a mutated BRCA gene, but it

doesn't go completely to zero. There is still a very small risk of developing breast cancer even after surgery because breast tissue is located not just in the breast but also in surrounding tissues, making it nearly impossible to remove it all. There are other treatment options, too, but they're not quite as effective as surgery. Some physicians recommend a drug called tamoxifen for women at high risk who choose not to have surgery—it reduces the cancer risk by about 50%.

What Is Peace of Mind Worth?

And what about just peace of mind? Surgeons report that 10% of women in their 40s who undergo surgery for breast cancer are now asking to have their healthy breast removed as well. For these cancer survivors, not having to worry about mammograms, biopsies, or breast surgery ever again may be the motivating factor. Some surgeons worry that these cancer survivors may not fully understand that if they are not carrying a mutated BRCA gene, removal of the healthy breast apparently has no effect on long-term survival. But who's to say what their motivation is, or to question their choices?

We've been talking about probabilities of cancer and even death in an impersonal way, as if this were a game of numbers. But this is not a game. Each of us may have to make difficult choices for ourselves or for a loved one some day. We'll be forced to balance personal feelings against impersonal odds. René Syler did not have mutated forms of either the BRCA1 or BRCA2 gene, but her family history and her own personal history of pre-cancerous changes in her breast tissue put her at high risk. So René Syler made a choice. She says she's happy with what she calls her "teenaged breasts" and with the knowledge that she'll never need another mammogram or biopsy. It may not be a choice you could make, but she still thinks it was the right choice for her.

Questions to consider

1 Blood tests for BRCA1 and BRCA2 are readily available. Are you planning to be tested? Why or why not?

2 If you knew that you had a mutated BRCA gene, would it change what you do or how you live?

3 What would you want your mother/wife/girlfriend/daughter to do if it she had a mutated BRCA gene?

The facts...

- Heritable mutations of two genes known as BRCA1 and BRCA2 are strongly associated with breast and ovarian cancer.
- Ovarian cancer often goes undetected until it is too late. The five-year survival rate is still under 40%.
- Some women are opting for prophylactic breast and ovary removal while they are still healthy.

Chapter 14 from *The Jungle*

Upton Sinclair

Upton Sinclair was born in 1878 in Baltimore and grew up in New York. He attended the City College of New York and Columbia University, but dropped out to devote himself to writing. His first novel, Springtime and Harvest, *appeared in 1901. In 1904 he published* Manassas, *at which time he joined the Socialist Party of America. The next year he founded with the novelist Jack London the Intercollegiate Socialist Society. Among his other novels are* King Coal *(1917);* Oil! *(1927), the basis for the movie* There Will Be Blood; Boston *(1928);* The Wet Parade *(1931); and* Dragon's Teeth *(1942). His fiction and non-fiction dealt with his concerns about wage labor, and the mining and oil industries, as well as the health hazards of the food industry, as reflected in* The Jungle *(1906). Sinclair was nominated for the Nobel Prize by Bernard Shaw and won the Pulitzer Prize in 1943. In 1967 President Lyndon Johnson invited Sinclair to the White House on the occasion of the signing of new food law legislation. Sinclair died the next year.* The Jungle, *a classic exposure of corruption, led to political action. In the following excerpt from Sinclair's famous work, the author offers a grim indictment of Chicago's meatpacking industry as it existed in the late 19th and early 20th centuries.*

1 With one member trimming beef in a cannery, and another working in a sausage factory, the family had a first-hand knowledge of the great majority of Packingtown swindles. For it was the custom, as they found, whenever meat was so spoiled that it could not be used for anything else, either to can it or else to

Reprinted from *Appeal to Reason*, February-November, 1905.

chop it up into sausages. With what had been told them by Jonas, who had worked in the pickle rooms, they could now study the whole of the spoiled-meat industry on the inside, and read a new and grim meaning into that old Packingtown jest—that they use everything of the pig except the squeal.

Jonas had told them how the meat that was taken out of pickle would often be found sour, and how they would rub it up with soda to take away the smell, and sell it to be eaten on free-lunch counters; also of all the miracles of chemistry which they performed, giving to any sort of meat, fresh or salted, whole or chopped, any colour and any flavour, and any odour they chose. In the pickling of hams they had an ingenious apparatus by which they saved time and increased the capacity of the plant—a machine consisting of a hollow needle attached to a pump; by plunging this needle into the meat and working with his foot, a man could fill a ham with pickle in a few seconds. And yet, in spite of this, there would be hams found spoiled, some of them with an odour so bad that a man could hardly bear to be in the room with them. To pump into these the packers had a second and much stronger pickle which destroyed the odour—a process known to the workers as 'giving them thirty per cent'. Also, after the hams had been smoked, there would be found some that had gone to the bad. Formerly these had been sold as 'Number Three Grade', but later on some ingenious person had hit upon a new device, and now they would extract the bone, about which the bad part generally lay, and insert in the hole a white-hot iron. After this invention there was no longer Number One, Two, and Three Grade—there was only Number One Grade. The packers were always originating such schemes—they had what they called 'boneless hams', which were all the odds and ends of pork stuffed into casings; and 'California hams', which were the shoulders, with big knuckle-joints, and nearly all the meat cut out; and fancy 'skinned hams', which were made of the oldest hogs, whose skins were so heavy and coarse that no one would buy them—that is, until they had been cooked and chopped fine and labelled 'head cheese'!

It was only when the whole ham was spoiled that it came into the department of Elzbieta. Cut up by the two-thousand-revolutions-a-minute flyers, and mixed with half a ton of other meat, no odour that ever was in a ham could make any difference. There was never the least attention paid to what was cut up for sausages; there would come all the way back from Europe old sausage that had been rejected, and that was mouldy and white—it would be dosed with borax and glycerine, and dumped into the hoppers, and made over again for home consumption. There would be meat that had tumbled out on the floor, in the dirt and sawdust, where the workers had tramped and spit uncounted billions of consumption germs. There would be meat stored in great piles in rooms; and the water from leaky roofs would drip over it, and thousands of rats would race about on it. It was too dark in these storage places to see well, but a man could run his hand over these piles of meat and sweep off handfuls of the dried dung of rats. These rats were nuisances, and the packers would put poisoned bread out for them; they would die, and then rats, bread, and meat would go into the hoppers together. This is no fairy story and no joke; the meat would be shovelled into carts, and the man who did the shovelling would not trouble to lift out a rat even when he saw one—there were things that went into the sausage in comparison with which a poisoned rat was a tidbit. There was no place for the men to wash their hands before they ate their dinner, and so they made a practice of washing them in the water that was to be ladled into the sausage. There were the butt ends of smoked meat, and the scraps of corned beef, and all the odds and ends of the waste of the plants, that would be dumped into old barrels in the cellar and left there. Under the system of rigid economy which the packers enforced, there were some jobs that it only paid to do once in a long time, and among these was the cleaning out of the waste barrels. Every spring they did it; and in the barrels would be dirt and rust, and old nails and stale water—and cartload after cartload of it would be taken up and dumped into the hoppers with fresh meat, and sent out to the public's breakfast. Some of it they would make into 'smoked' sausage—but as the smoking took time, and was therefore expensive, they would call upon their chemistry department, and preserve it with borax and colour it with gelatine to make it brown. All of their sausage came out of the same bowl, but when they came to wrap it they would stamp some of it 'special', and for this they would charge two cents more a pound.

Such were the new surroundings in which Elzbieta was placed, and such was the work she was compelled to do. It was stupefying, brutalizing work; it left her no time to think, no strength for anything. She was part of the machine she tended, and every faculty that was not needed for the machine was doomed to be crushed out of existence. There was only one mercy about the cruel grind—that it gave her the gift of insensibility. Little by little she sank into a torpor—she fell silent. She would meet Jurgis and Ona in the evening, and the three would walk home together, often without saying a word. Ona, too, was falling into a habit of silence—Ona, who had once gone about singing like a bird. She was sick and miserable, and often she would barely have strength enough to drag herself home. And there they would eat what they had to eat, and afterwards, because there was only their misery to talk of, they would crawl into bed and fall into a stupor, and never stir until it was time to get up again, and dress by candle-light, and go back to the machines. They were so numbed that they did not even suffer much from hunger now; only the children continued to fret when the food ran short.

5   Yet the soul of Ona was not dead—the souls of none of them were dead, but only sleeping. And now and then they would waken, and these were cruel times. The gates of memory would roll open; old joys would stretch out their arms to them, old hopes and dreams would call to them, and they would stir beneath the burden that lay upon them, and feel its forever immeasurable weight. They could not even cry out beneath it; but anguish would seize them, more dreadful than the agony of death. It was a thing scarcely to be spoken—a thing never spoken by all the world, that will not know its own defeat.

They were beaten; they had lost the game; they were swept aside. It was not less tragic because it was so sordid, because that it had to do with wages and grocery bills and rents. They had dreamed of freedom; of a chance to look about them and learn something; to be decent and clean; to see their child grow up to be strong. And now it was all gone—it would never be! They had played the game and they had lost. Six years more of toil they had to face before they could expect the least respite, the cessation of the payments upon the house; and how cruelly certain it was that they could never stand six years of such a life as they were living! They were lost, they were going down, and there was no deliverance for them, no hope; for all the help it gave them the vast city in which they lived might have been an ocean waste, a wilderness, a desert, a tomb. So often this mood would come to Ona in the nighttime, when something wakened her. She would lie, afraid of the beating of her own heart, fronting the blood-red eyes of the old primeval terror of life. Once she cried aloud and woke Jurgis, who was tired and cross. After that she learned to weep silently. Their moods so seldom came together now. It was as if their hopes were buried in separate graves.

Jurgis, being a man, had troubles of his own. There was another spectre following him. He had never spoken of it, nor would he allow anyone else to speak of it—he had never acknowledged its existence to himself. Yet the battle with it took all the manhood that he had—and once or twice, alas! a little more. Jurgis had discovered drink.

He was working in the steaming pit of hell, day after day, week after week, until now there was not an organ of his body that did its work without pain, until the sound of ocean breakers echoed in his head day and night, and the building swayed and danced before him as he went down the street. And from all the unending horror of this there was a respite, a deliverance—he could drink! He could forget the pain, he could slip off the burden; he would see clearly again, he would be master of his brain, of his thoughts, of his will. His dead self would stir in him, and he would find himself laughing and cracking jokes with his companions. He would be a man again, and master of his life.

It was not an easy thing for Jurgis to take more than two or three drinks. With the first drink he could eat a meal, and he could persuade himself that that was economy; with the second he could eat another meal. But there would come a time when he could eat no more, and then to pay for a drink was an unthinkable extravagance, a defiance of the age-long instincts of his hunger-haunted class. One day, however, he took the plunge, and drank up all that he had in his pockets, and went home half 'piped', as the men phrase it. He was happier than he had been in a year; and yet, because he knew that the happiness would not last, he was savage, too—with those who would wreck it, and with the world, and with his life. And then, again, beneath this, he was sick with the shame of himself. Afterward, when he saw the despair of his family, and reckoned up the money he had spent, the tears came into his eyes, and he began the long battle with the spectre.

10 It was a battle that had no end, that never could have one. But 10 Jurgis did not realize that very clearly; he was not given much time for reflection. He simply knew that he was always fighting. Steeped in misery and despair as he was, merely to walk down the street was to be put upon the rack. There was surely a saloon on the corner—perhaps on all four corners, and some in the middle of the block as well; and each one stretched out a hand to him—each one had a personality of its own, allurements unlike any other. Going and coming—before sunrise and after dark—there was warmth and a glow of light, and the

steam of hot food, and perhaps music, or a friendly face, and a word of good cheer. Jurgis developed a fondness for having Ona on his arm whenever he went out on the street, and he would hold her tightly, and walk fast. It was pitiful to have Ona know of this—it drove him wild to think of it; the thing was not fair, for Ona had never tasted drink, and could not understand. Sometimes, in desperate hours, he would find himself wishing that she might learn what it was, so that he need not be ashamed in her presence. They might drink together, and escape from the horror—escape for a while, come what would.

So there came a time when nearly all the conscious life of Jurgis consisted of a struggle with the craving for liquor. He would have ugly moods, when he hated Ona and the whole family, because they stood in his way. He was a fool to have married; he had tied himself down, had made himself a slave. It was all because he was a married man that he was compelled to stay in the yards; if it had not been for that he might have gone off like Jonas, and to hell with the packers. There were few single men in the fertilizer mill—and those few were working only for a chance to escape. Meantime, too, they had something to think about while they worked—they had the memory of the last time they had been drunk, and the hope of the time when they would be drunk again. As for Jurgis, he was expected to bring home every penny; he could not even go with the men at noon-time—he was supposed to sit down and eat his dinner on a pile of fertilizer dust.

This was not always his mood, of course; he still loved his family. But just now was a time of trial. Poor little Antanas, for instance— who had never failed to win him with a smile—little Antanas was not smiling just now, being a mass of fiery red pimples. He had had all the diseases that babies are heir to in quick succession—scarlet fever, mumps, and whooping-cough in the first year, and now he was down with measles. There was no one to attend to him but Kotrina; there was no doctor to help him because they were too poor, and children did not die of the measles—at least, not often. Now and then Kotrina would find time to sob over his woes, but for the greater part of the time he had to be left alone, barricaded upon the bed. The floor was full of draughts, and if he caught cold he would die. At night he was tied down, lest he should kick the covers off him, while the family lay in their stupor of exhaustion. He would lie and scream for hours, almost in convulsions; and then, when he was worn out, he would lie whimpering and wailing in his torment. He was burning up with fever, and his eyes were running sores; in the day-time he was a thing uncanny and impish to behold, a plaster of pimples and sweat, a great purple lump of misery.

Yet all this was not really as cruel as it sounds, for, sick as he was, little Antanas was the least unfortunate member of that family. He was quite able to bear his sufferings—it was as if he had all these complaints to show what a prodigy of health he was. He was the child of his parents' youth and joy; he grew up like the conjuror's rose-bush, and all the world was his oyster. In general, he toddled around the kitchen all day with a lean and hungry look—the portion of the family's allowance that fell to him was not enough, and he was unrestrainable in his demand for more. Antanas was but little over a year old, and already no one but his father could manage him.

It seemed as if he had taken all of his mother's strength—had left nothing for those that might come after him. Ona was with child again now, and it was a dreadful thing to contemplate; even Jurgis, dumb and despairing as he was, could not but understand that yet other agonies were on the way, and shudder at the thought of them.

15 For Ona was visibly going to pieces. In the first place she was developing a cough, like the one that had killed old Dede Antanas. She had had a trace of it ever since that fatal morning when the greedy streetcar corporation had turned her out into the rain; but now it was beginning to grow serious, and to wake her up at night. Even worse than that was the fearful nervousness from which she suffered; she would have frightful headaches and fits of aimless weeping; and sometimes she would come home at night shuddering and moaning, and would fling herself down upon the bed and burst into tears. Several times she was quite beside herself and hysterical; and then Jurgis would go half mad with fright. Elzbieta would explain to him that it could not be helped, that a woman was subject to such things when she was pregnant; but he was hardly to be persuaded, and would beg and plead to know what had happened. She had never been like this before, he would argue; it was monstrous and unthinkable. It was the life she had to live, the accursed work she had to do, that was killing her by inches. She was not fitted for it—no woman was fitted for it, no woman ought to be allowed to do such work; if the world could not keep them alive any other way it ought to kill them at once and be done with it. They ought not to marry, to have children; no working man ought to marry. If he, Jurgis, had known what a woman was like, he would have had his eyes torn out first. So he would carry on, becoming half hysterical himself, which was an unbearable thing to

see in a big man; Ona would pull herself together and fling herself into his arms, begging him to stop, to be still, that she would be better, it would be all right. So she would lie and sob out her grief upon his shoulder, while he gazed at her, as helpless as a wounded animal, the target of unseen enemies.

The Food Police

Julie Guthman

Julie Guthman received a Ph.D. in Geography from the University of California at Berkeley. She is the author of Agrarian Dreams: The Paradox of Organic Farming in California, *published in 2004 by the University of California Press, which says that "Guthman casts doubt on the current wisdom about organic food and agriculture and [refutes] popular portrayals of organic agriculture as a small-scale family farm endeavor in opposition to 'industrial' agriculture." She has published widely on the subject of how food is distributed and produced. As a professor in the Community Studies department at the University of California at Santa Cruz, her research focus, as her website states, is on "sustainable agriculture and alternative food movements, international political economy of food and agriculture, politics of obesity, political ecology, race and food, and critical human geography." At the University of California Humanities Research Institute, she completed a project that looked at the race and class politics of food reform particularly as it relates to the "epidemic of obesity." A short list of her articles in professional journals includes "Teaching the Politics of Obesity" (2009); "Bringing Good Food to Others: Investigating the Subjects of Alternative Food Practice" (2008); "'If Only They Knew:' Colorblindness and Universalism in California Food Institutions"; and "Commentary on Teaching Food: Why I Am Fed Up with Michael Pollan et al" (2007). She has received the 2004 Ashby Prize; the 2007 Frederick H. Buttel Award for Outstanding Achievement from the Rural Sociological Society (for* Agrarian Dreams*); and the*

Reprinted from *Gastronomica* (2007), by permission of the University of California Press.

2009 Donald Q. Innes Award from the Association of American Geographers. In the following selection, excerpted from Gastronomica *and reprinted in* Utne Reader, *Guthman charges that Michael Pollan "reinforces the belief that some people—thin people—clearly must have seen the light that the rest are blind to."*

1 I t has become common to speak of an "epidemic of obesity." News sources routinely feature articles on obesity, and some even suggest that the obesity epidemic is one of the greatest public health threats of our times, perhaps rivaling AIDS or avian flu. Obesity is commonly linked to other social problems as well. It has been named as a cost to businesses in terms of worker productivity, a cause for poor pupil performance, a weight-load problem for airlines, and a security threat in terms of military preparedness. Proposed and implemented social solutions have included snack taxes, corporate-sponsored exercise breaks, stronger food labeling laws, and state-mandated student weigh-ins at public schools.

Obesity is a bonanza for social reformers who deploy the rhetoric of fat in support of projects from farm-to-school programs to mixed-use housing and transportation centers; and for puritans who use fatness as an example of the moral decrepitude to which we must just say no. Finally, the obesity epidemic, and its tendency to dignify obsessions that equate thinness and beauty, is hugely profitable, contributing, by some estimates, to a $40 billion-per-year weight-loss industry. Television shows like *The Biggest Loser*, sponsored by purveyors of diet foods, fitness centers, and pharmaceuticals, contribute to the false idea that diets work, thereby increasing the market for such goods and services. And if the daily spam I receive for Anatrim is any indication, the underground market in pharmaceuticals is cashing in, too.

A rash of popular books on the so-called obesity epidemic take a variety of positions, though virtually all claim to tell the real story about the epidemic and who is gaining by it. For example, J. Eric Oliver's *Fat Politics: The Real Story Behind America's Obesity Epidemic*, while voicing skepticism of the ways in which obesity has been framed, contributes to the frenzy through its tone.

Lately, another group of writers has gotten in on the act. More refined and measured, their books turn on the theme of "what to eat"—which is actually the title of Marion Nestle's most recent volume.

Other books include Peter Singer's *The Way We Eat: Why Our Food Choices Matter*, Anna Lappé's *Grub: Ideas for an Urban Organic Kitchen*, and Jane Goodall's *Harvest for Hope: A Guide to Mindful Eating*. The sine qua non is Michael Pollan's *The Omnivore's Dilemma: A Natural History of Four Meals*. It is like no other because not only does Pollan know his stuff, he also can write his way out of a paper bag, and his book sales show it. Virtually all of these authors extol the virtues of the organic and the local while arguing for a commonsense, ecumenical approach to diet choices. That makes them refreshing in relation to the usual weight-loss books and painfully restrictive messages of latter-day health foodism. Or does it?

5   Many of these authors share a common rhetorical strategy. They refer to the statistics of rising obesity rates, the surfeit of calories taken in relative to those expended, and the inexorable road toward illness with concomitant rising health care costs. They go on to discuss the ubiquity of fast, junky food in order to make their points about what constitutes "real" food. But whereas most of the popular writers on fat attribute growing obesity to a variety of culprits—watching television, long drive-to-work times, supermarket product placement, working mothers, baggy clothes, marketing to children, poverty, affluence, and modernity, basically everything under the sun—Pollan's analysis is more pointed. As he puts it, "All these explanations are true, as far as they go. But it pays to go a little further, to search for the cause behind the causes. Which, very simply, is this: When food is abundant and cheap, people will eat more of it and get fat." Pollan then points to the culprit: corn.

He tells a compelling story about how corn has become the foundation of the national diet. He traces this first to the transport of corn from what is now Mexico to points north, where it took hold and outdid wheat in yield and ease of cultivation. But corn's strength turned to its weakness; it was prone to systematic overproduction in U.S. agriculture, so surpluses ended up to no good. Corn whiskey was the beverage of choice in pre-Prohibition drinking binges. Since the 1970s, national farm policy has buttressed overproduction with subsidies. Pollan reminds us that corn is omnipresent in a fast-food meal: the high fructose corn syrup that sweetens the soda: the feed of the steer that goes into the hamburger; often the oil that fries the potatoes; an ingredient in the bun. Processed food, Pollan argues, makes us *walking corn*, and the "Alcoholic Republic" has now given way to "the Republic of Fat."

Pollan's critique of the cost-cutting measures of the fast-food giants, the nutritional impoverishment of processed food, and an agricultural subsidy system that encourages ecologically problematic monoculture, horrendous animal treatment, and food dumping in the name of "aid" is spot-on. I could think of no clearer path to a more ecologically sound and socially just food system than the removal of those subsidies. Yet, in evoking obesity, Pollan turns our gaze from farm policy to the fat body. Should fat people bear the weight of this argument?

There is much to criticize in the public conversation about obesity. The evidentiary basis of an "epidemic" is weak, as it relies on changes in average body mass index, a contested way to measure obesity. Moreover, the relationship between food intake, exercise, and growing obesity is poorly understood. Michael Gard and Jan Wright's exhaustive review of research shows that the notion that weight gain results from a surplus of calories has not been borne out; at best, caloric metabolism appears to explain less than half of body size variation. Finally, claims that obesity is a primary cause of disease are filled with logical flaws, chief among them that obesity may be symptomatic of diseases such as type 2 diabetes. Gard and Wright argue that obesity research itself has become so entangled with moral discourses and aesthetic values that the "science of obesity" can no longer speak for itself.

Many authors of the recent popular books on diet seem unaware of how obesity messages work as admonishment. According to Paul Campos, author of *The Obesity Myth: Why America's Obsession with Weight Is Hazardous to Your Health*, the people most personally affected by discussions of obesity are those who want to lose 10 or 15 pounds, despite the fact that those who are "overweight" by current standards have longer life spans than those who are "thin" or "normal." In a course I taught, Politics of Obesity, I was not surprised by the number of students who wrote in their journals of their hidden "fatness" or eating disorders. The number of entries that stated how the course itself had produced body anxiety and intensified concern over diet and exercise, however, was shocking, given that much of the material was critical of obesity talk. The philosopher Michel Foucault might have called this the "productive" power of obesity talk—naming a behavior as a problem intensifies anxiety about that behavior. Yet entirely absent from the pages of the recent popular books is any authorial reflection on how obesity talk further stigmatizes those who are fat, or on how this social scolding might work at cross-purposes to health and well-being.

10   But there is something even more disturbing about these books. Pollan claims that people eat corn because it's there. They are dupes. Jane Goodall makes a similar leap when she writes, "There is no mechanism that turns off the desire—instinct, really—to eat food when it is available." Even Marion Nestle's concern with supermarket aisles suggests that people mechanically react to product placement. This raises an important question: Why are Pollan, Goodall, and Nestle not fat? If junk food is so ubiquitous that it cannot be resisted, how is it that some people remain thin?   10

It appears that these authors see themselves as morally superior to fat people in the sense that they characterize fat people as being short of subjectivity. Goodall makes the above assertion having just written of "sad," "overweight," "overindulged" cats and dogs being "killed by kindness," seeming to equate fat people with pets. In the "documentary" *Super Size Me*, virtually all shots of fat people are headless. Some might argue that having no personal identifiers protects fat people in the camera's eye, but headlessness also invokes mindlessness. Moreover, protection assumes that fat people are ashamed of their bodies and their eating habits. This presumption is precisely the problem that Kathleen LeBesco captures in *Revolting Bodies? The Struggle to Redefine Fat Identity*, including her critique of the fat acceptance movement itself. At best fat people are seen as victims of food, genetic codes, or metabolism; at worst, they are slovenly, stupid, or without resolve. Meanwhile, she notes, many thin people can indulge in all manner of unhealthy behaviors without being called to account for their body size. In other words, fat people are imbued with little subjectivity no matter what they do, while thin people are imbued with heightened subjectivity no matter what they do.

This is the most pernicious aspect of the analysis by Pollan and others. If junk food is everywhere and people are naturally drawn to it, those who resist it must have heightened powers. When Pollan waxes poetic about his own rarefied, distinctive eating practices, the messianic, self-satisfied tone is not accidental. In describing his ability to overcome King Corn, to conceive, procure, prepare, and serve his version of the perfect meal, Pollan affirms himself as a supersubject while relegating others to objects of education, intervention, or just plain scorn.

Even if it were true that obesity is a public health threat, even if it could be proven that it results from fast-food consumption, and even if we didn't care about stigmatizing obesity or treating fat people as objects, is Pollan's way the way out? At the end of a book whose biggest strength is a section that lays out the environmental history and political economy of corn, his answer, albeit oblique, is to eat like he does. The meal that he helped forage and hunt and cooked all by himself, as he puts it, "gave me the opportunity, so rare in modern life, to eat in full consciousness of everything involved in feeding myself: For once, I was able to pay the full karmic price of a meal." To what kind of politics does this lead? Despite his early focus on corn subsidies, Pollan does not urge his readers to write to their congressional representatives about the folly of such subsidies, to comment to the Food and Drug Administration about food additives, or, for that matter, to sabotage fields where genetically engineered corn is grown.

Indeed, he makes no suggestion that we ought to alter the structure of the food system so that all might come to eat better. Pollan betrays himself in his admiration of Joel Salatin, a beyond-organic farmer who denounces federal regulation as an impediment to building a viable local food chain.

15   Unfortunately, this antiregulatory approach to food politics has 15 taken hold. I have read countless undergraduate papers that begin with the premise that the global food system is anomic and that "if people only knew where their food came from," food provisioning would evolve to be more ecological, humane, and just. Many of my students have strong convictions that they should and can teach people how and what to eat, as if you could "change the world one meal at a time" without attention to policy.

I worry that Michael Pollan reinforces this privileged and apolitical idea and reinforces the belief that some people—thin people— clearly must have seen the light that the rest are blind to. Pollan is a damn good writer and a smart man, which makes *The Omnivore's Dilemma* a compelling read. But I can't stomach where it leads. In a funny way, it makes me crave corn-based Cheetos.

Heart and Blood Vessels

A colored arteriogram of a healthy heart.

Comparative Effectiveness Research

Mr. Reynolds has a heart problem. An angiogram shows that a short section of one of the main arteries supplying the left ventricle of his heart is narrowed, restricting blood flow to his heart muscle. His doctor tells him that he is at serious risk of a heart attack. The doctor explains that there are at least three techniques that could be used to restore blood flow to his heart: 1) balloon angioplasty, 2) placement of a coronary artery stent, or 3) a coronary artery bypass graft (CABG). Which would be best for Mr. Reynolds? They go over the options together, but to Mr. Reynolds it seems like comparing

apples to oranges, and he isn't sure he understands. He leaves the decision to his physician, whom he has known for 25 years. In the end the physician chooses the technique that has worked best for his previous patients.

The body of medical literature is now so vast and expanding so rapidly that even the best physicians can't know it all. This is where a relatively new field of medical science called "Comparative Effectiveness Research" (CER) comes in. CER focuses solely on analyzing the medical literature already available, in order to reach

scientifically sound judgments about the value (or lack of value) of specific medical tests, treatments, and disease prevention strategies. In essence, CER seeks to determine the best practices in medicine based on our current knowledge.

Changing How Medicine is Practiced

Consider how CER might benefit Mr. Reynolds' physician (and Mr. Reynolds, of course). By reviewing CER data, Mr. Reynolds' physician might learn that a stent is considered most effective for a middle-aged white male, but that there's an age-related tipping point; if the patient is over 55, balloon angioplasty is the better option. (Hmmm, how old *is* Mr. Reynolds this year?) CER might also be able to tell the physician whether the treatment of choice depends on the severity of the narrowing—if the degree of narrowing of a coronary artery is greater than 80%, for example, then the best option (again, for a middle-aged white male) would be a coronary artery bypass graft rather than balloon angioplasty. (What is the degree of narrowing in Mr. Reynolds, anyway?) Toss in other factors like gender, race, physical condition, body weight, smoker-versus-nonsmoker, and you can begin to see the full power of CER. In theory, CER could analyze multiple factors at once to arrive at the best treatment option for patients who are described by a particular combination of factors. Even the most experienced physicians don't carry *that* much information around in their heads!

Some politicians believe that little investment in CER now could pay for itself in reduced health care expenditures in the future. To jump-start a national CER program, Congress passed the "Comparative Effectiveness Research Act of 2009" and funded it with $1.1 billion as part of the economic stimulus package. To keep the program free of bias, the prestigious Institute of Medicine of the National Academies of Science was asked to come up with a list of 100 top priority topics for CER funding. Among the topics are comparisons of the most effective practices to treat or prevent a number of cardiovascular diseases and risk factors, including high blood pressure, coronary artery disease, heart failure, and abnormalities of heart electrical rhythm. This is not surprising, since cardiovascular diseases are the number one cause of death in the United States (cancer is second).

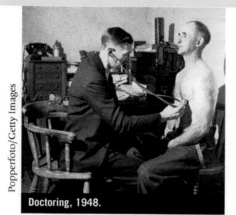

Popperfoto/Getty Images

Doctoring, 1948.

Who Will Make Health Care Decisions?

CER could become a powerful tool for improving health care quality and lowering costs. Nevertheless, the CER Act of 2009 has stirred strong feelings among physicians, patients, politicians, and the health care industry because of the ways it could change how medicine is practiced. Physicians and patient advocacy groups worry that if "best practices" become defined by CER, doctors and patients could begin to lose the right to make decisions regarding treatment options. They fear that health care decisions may be dictated primarily by bureaucrats and insurance companies. In recognition of this concern, the legislation included language to the effect that the outcomes of CER research are not to be used to develop required or mandated guidelines when it comes to treatment decisions, payment, or insurance coverage, including Medicare/Medicaid coverage. In other words, physicians and patients can still use their best judgment in deciding upon the appropriate treatment option, regardless of what CER shows, at least for now.

But therein lies the big question: Will physicians and patients continue to be the decision makers in medical treatment decisions? Or is it inevitable that the old way

of practicing medicine is going to change? Do we really believe that health insurance companies, group health plans, and even Medicare/Medicaid will *not* find a way to use CER data to "influence" reimbursement policies, and hence treatment decisions? Would it be a good thing or a bad thing if they did?

Flash forward 25 years. It's you in the doctor's office now, and the doctor is telling you that your cardiac scan shows a 63% narrowing of a section of your left-anterior descending coronary artery. She swings around to her computer, taps a few keys, and reports that according to the latest data analysis from the Comparative Effectiveness Research Institute, the current most effective method for repair of your coronary artery is "Robotic Artificial Vessel Extension" (RAVE), and that your government-supported health insurance will pay for it. A few more taps and she informs you that there is an opening on the hospital's surgical schedule on Tuesday and that Dr. Sloan is available to do your surgery. She adds that 99.7% of Dr. Sloan's surgeries of this type have been successful, and that 94% of all patients with your condition are discharged from the hospital on the same day as the surgery. You go home to your wife with the good news, and tell her to go ahead and book that vacation to London next month.

B Busco/Getty Images

Doctoring in the 21st century.

Questions to consider

1 Who do you want to help you decide which treatment options would be best for you? If it's not a specific person or position (doctor, patient representative, health insurance specialist), what information would you like to have available to you?

2 Do you think cost-effectiveness should be a part of any comparative effectiveness analysis of treatment or diagnostic options? Why or why not?

VStock/Alamy

Soybeans. Over 90% of the U. S. soybean crop is genetically modified.

Genetically Engineered Plants

Current Issue

By now you have almost certainly eaten food products that came from *genetically engineered* (GE) plants. GE plants are plants that have been genetically engineered to contain specific genes for a specific purpose. They have been cultivated commercially since 1994. But should these plants have been developed in the first place? Now that we have them, what should we do about it?

Nearly all GE plants are *transgenic*, meaning that they contain foreign genes taken from some other species of organism (a few GE plants are *cisgenic*—containing genes or gene deletions from the same species). Nearly all of the current commercially important GE plants contain genes that either allow the plant to produce its own insecticide (insect-killer) or that make the plant resistant to one of the most common herbicides (weed-killers).

GE Plants Offer Many Benefits

Now that GE crops have been around a while, it is clear that they offer many benefits. GE crops have reduced the cost of crop production for farmers because they can spray less often and use fewer toxic chemicals. This in turn is a net benefit to the environment, both in terms of the reduced use of toxic chemicals and in the reduced need for fuel for farm equipment. An even greater benefit to the environment may be in the reduced need to till fields to control weeds. Less tilling to control weeds means less soil erosion, and therefore less soil and fertilizer runoff into streams and rivers. Farmers and food processors in the United States seem to have accepted the benefits of GE crops, as judged by the trends in crop and processed foods production. It is estimated that 70–75% of all processed foods in U.S. supermarkets contain GE ingredients. In 2009, 85% of the U.S. corn crop and a whopping 91% of the soybean crop came from GE plants.

AGStockUSA/Scott Sinklier

Maize that has been genetically modified to resist an herbicide. A concern is that GM crops could cross-pollinate with non-GM crops.

In theory, consumers should benefit from GE plants as well, as the reduced cost of crop production is passed on up the food production chain. GE plants with direct benefits to consumers are less common yet, though many are in the development stage. Scientists are working on plants that will produce edible vaccines, valuable human proteins, and even drugs.

GE Plants Are Not Without Risks

Many people worry that GE plants are not as beneficial as they might seem, and they are concerned that GE plants may not have been tested rigorously for safety before they were widely adapted. Although resistance to GE plants seems to be dying down in the United States, farmers and consumers in Europe still have their doubts. The concerns are legitimate, even if the potential risks have not yet been proven.

Are GE foods safe to eat?

In the United States, the safety of GE foods is monitored by the FDA. So far there is no scientific evidence that any currently approved GE food product is dangerous, despite the fact that millions of us are eating them every day. Nevertheless, we would be wise to remain vigilant. A recent report by the U.S. General Accounting Office concluded

that the FDA's current regulation of GE foods is adequate but could be improved. Suggested improvements include making the FDA evaluation process more straightforward and less burdensome, and randomly checking the food companies' data.

Do GE plants endanger the environment?

Some environmental concerns about GE plants are that they may endanger nonharmful insects, that they will cross-pollinate with conventional non-GE food plants, and that cross-pollination of herbicide-resistant GE plants with weeds will create "superweeds" resistant to herbicides.

Some non-harmful insects might be killed as a consequence of ingesting too much pollen from insect-resistant GE crops. Such a consequence, however, should be weighed against the benefits of not having to spray so often with insecticides, which is also likely to kill non-harmful insects.

More problematic is the possibility of cross-pollination. Studies show that transgenes have already spread from GE corn in the United States to conventional maize in Mexico, and that other food crops in the United States have been contaminated by their GE counterparts as well. Whether this might create a problem in the future is unknown. However, research is already beginning to address the issue. "Terminator technologies" are under development that could render the seeds of GE plants sterile in the second generation, or that could prevent GE plants from expressing the novel gene unless the plant is treated with a special "gene unlocking" chemical. However, social scientists worry that terminator technologies will prevent poor farmers from benefiting from GE crops because they will not be able to save seed for planting the next year—they'll have to buy GE seed (or the unlocking chemical) each year from the agribusiness that holds the patent.

As for the development of superweeds, scientists agree that it could happen, just as many bacteria are becoming resistant to antibiotics. One way to slow the evolution

of resistant weeds would be to spray with different kinds of herbicides occasionally.

Public Resistance Inhibits GE Crop Development

Despite the general findings of a lack of significant harm by GE crops so far, public resistance remains high in some countries. In Europe, protesters still conduct raids on GE crops, destroying them before harvest. The European Union requires food producers to monitor GE crops at all stages of production, and any product that contains more than 0.9% GE ingredients must be labeled accordingly. In Australia and New Zealand, all GE foods intended for sale must undergo a premarket safety assessment by a government agency. In some cases these regulations effectively amount to trade barriers for GE food products, most of which come from the United States or Canada. The resistance has had a chilling effect on GE foods research, development, and commercialization.

Robert Brook/Photo Researchers

Some countries require that foods containing genetically engineered ingredients be labeled.

Angry rhetoric will not solve this dilemma. GE crops appear to be here to stay. We need to learn how to harness this new technology for the public good. We need simplified but effective regulations that protect consumers and the environment from potentially harmful practices, while at the same time permitting practices that may be beneficial.

Questions to consider

1 Do you approve of the widespread planting of GE food crops? Do you feel comfortable eating them?

2 GE foods are created for a variety of reasons, from resistance to herbicides to the delivery of vaccines and vitamins. Should we permit the development of some GE foods and not others, and if so, which ones? Defend your position.

The facts...

- Genetically engineered (GE) plants contain genes from other plants, bacteria, or even animals.
- Over 85% of all of the corn and soybeans in the United States come from GE plants.
- The use of GE crops has improved crop yields, lowered crop production costs, and reduced some aspects of environmental damage.
- Whether GE crops pose any long-term health or environmental risks is not yet fully known.
- GE food testing and labeling requirements in some countries threaten the export of GE food crops from the United States and Canada.

Curves Ahead: How to Eat and Exercise Your Way to Great Shape

Randi Glatzer

Randi Glatzer (1962 –) received her B.A. in English from the State University of New York at Binghamton in 1984. She became interested in writing and journalism while writing for her college newspaper, Pipe Dream. *Her fist jobs were for local newspapers in New York and New Jersey, such as the* Times Herald Record *in Middletown, NY. She has written professionally since college—mostly about health and social issues. Currently, she is working on more investigative reporting on rape and the prison systems. She has been a contributing editor for* American Health *magazine and has regularly written for* Self, Mademoiselle, Good Housekeeping, Vibe, *the* Village Voice, *and* Money. *The article titled "Don't Hate Me Because I'm Thin," written from personal experience and was published in* Mademoiselle *in May of 1995. It gained attention as one of the first articles addressing the issue of being too thin in a world where most teenage and college girls are concerned with losing weight. At 5'6", Glatzer was 99 pounds in high school, and gained 10 pounds through weight lifting and nutrition. She now weighs 120 but has struggled with being too thin for her whole life. "Curves Ahead" was written as a response to the hundreds of letters* Mademoiselle *received about Glatzer's struggle—as a tool for how to actually gain weight. "Curves" was originally published in* Mademoiselle *in 1997.*

"Curves Ahead: How to Eat and Exercise Your Way to a Great Shape," by Randi Glatzer, reprinted from www.phys.com, adapted from *Mademoiselle*, May 1997.

[1] eing too thin isn't as common as being overweight, says Connie Diekman, R.D., a nutritionist in St. Louis. "But that doesn't mean it's an unimportant problem." (She estimates that one out of every 20 people who visits her office wants to gain, not lose.) So if you don't think being called "skinny" is a compliment, there's help. (P.S.: Even if you're not totally sylphlike, keep reading; there's useful info here about why you gain weight when you *don't* want to.)

Tip 1: Eat More, More Often

You may think you already *do* eat a ton—but often, people who think they're stuffing themselves all day are really gorging at one meal while eating sporadically the rest of the time. "The most important thing is to be consistent," advises Nancy Clark, M.S., R.D., author of *Nancy Clark's Sports Nutrition Guidebook,* second edition (Human Kinetics, 1997). Which means not skipping meals, ever: Each breakfast, lunch and dinner is an opportunity to increase your weight. To find out how much—or how little—you're consuming, Diekman suggests keeping a detailed food diary. Write down everything you eat and when. Then add up the calories. Once you know how far you're falling short, you can fix it.

Tip 2: Fill Up on Low Fat

Shoot for a pound-a-week gain. To do that, you'll need at least 3,500 extra calories a week or 500 more a day. And while sugar and fat are calorie-dense, a junk-food diet isn't healthful—and you'll end up feeling disgusting. Some *good*-yet-fattening foods to put on the menu:

> Juice: Drink juice instead of tea or water. A glass of o.j. has 110 calories.
> Granola: Eat a cup in the A.M. (400 calories) instead of Cheerios (110).
> Yogurt: A cup of Dannon strawberry plus a banana adds up to 345 calories.
> Bagels: Have one with two tablespoons of peanut butter (400 calories).
> Energy-to-go: One chocolate PowerBar packs 230 calories, and it fits in your pocket. Or mix up a shake. No need to use the

pricey powders from the health-food store; Carnation Instant Breakfast will work (220 calories).

Tip 3: Pump Iron

You may think you don't need to work out—you're thin enough already. But unless you exercise, whatever you gain will glom onto your body's so-called "storage areas," and you'll end up with a potbelly and scrawny chicken legs. Not pretty. Get friendly with weights, though, and you'll distribute the pounds all over.

For maximum impact, try weight machines, free weights or push-ups. Progressive resistance is key. In other words, once you can lift a three pound weight 15 times, work up to five pounds, then eight, then ten and so on. Do keep in mind, however, that all this exercise will speed up your (naturally fast) metabolism even more. So eat, eat, eat.

Tip 4: Give it Time

If nothing seems to work, be patient. Until age 25, your metabolism remains high because your bones are still packing in the calcium. But by age 30, or even your late twenties, your metabolic rate should start to slow down, making weight gain easier. So instead of dreading the approach of your fourth decade, you may be thrilled to find that it brings you newly sexy hips.

That Lean and Hungry Look

Suzanne Britt Jordan

Suzanne Britt Jordan was born in Winston-Salem, North Carolina. Educated at Salem College and Washington University, where she received an M.A. in English, she has taught English at Meredith College. Widely published, Jordan has written columns for North Carolina Gardens & Homes *and the* Dickens Dispatch *(a national newsletter for Charles Dickens devotees) and articles for the* Baltimore Sun, Books and Religion, *the* Boston Globe, Long Island Newsday, The New York Times, *and* Newsweek. *Her essays have been collected in* Skinny People Are Dull and Crunchy Like Carrots *(1982) and* Show and Tell *(1983). She has also published a history of Meredith College and two English textbooks. This essay, which appeared in* Newsweek *and in* Skinny People, *exhibits her casual yet perceptive writing style. As she touts the qualities of fat over thin, judge yourself, as Jordan might judge you!*

1   Caesar was right. Thin people need watching. I've been watching them for most of my adult life, and I don't like what I see. When these narrow fellows spring at me, I quiver to my toes. Thin people come in all personalities, most of them menacing. You've got your "together" thin person, your mechanical thin person, your condescending thin person, your tsk-tsk thin person, your efficiency-expert thin person. All of them are dangerous.

In the first place, thin people aren't fun. They don't know how to goof off, at least in the best, fat sense of the word. They've always got to be adoing. Give them a coffee break, and they'll jog around the block. Supply them with a quiet evening at home, and they'll fix the screen door and lick S&H green stamps. They say things like "there aren't enough hours in the day." Fat people never say that. Fat people think the day is too damn long already.

Thin people make me tired. They've got speedy little metabolisms that cause them to bustle briskly. They're forever rubbing their bony hands together and eyeing new problems to "tackle." I like to surround myself with sluggish, inert, easygoing fat people, the kind who believe that if you clean it up today, it'll just get dirty again tomorrow.

Some people say the business about the jolly fat person is a myth, that all of us chubbies are neurotic, sick, sad people. I disagree. Fat people may not be chortling all day long, but they're a hell of a lot *nicer* than the wizened and shriveled. Thin people turn surly, mean, and hard at a young age because they never learn the value of a hot-fudge sundae for easing tension. Thin people don't like gooey soft things because they themselves are neither gooey nor soft. They are crunchy and dull, like carrots. They go straight to the heart of the matter while fat people let things stay all blurry and hazy and vague, the way things actually are. Thin people want to face the truth. Fat people know there is no truth. One of my thin friends is always staring at complex, unsolvable problems and saying, "The key thing is. . . ." Fat people never say that. They know there isn't any such thing as the key thing about anything.

5   Thin people believe in logic. Fat people see all sides. The sides fat people see are rounded blobs, usually gray, always nebulous and truly not worth worrying about. But the thin person persists. "If you consume more calories than you burn," says one of my thin friends, "you will gain weight. It's that simple." Fat people always grin when they hear statements like that. They know better.

Fat people realize that life is illogical and unfair. They know very well that God is not in his heaven and all is not right with the world. If God is up there, fat people could have two doughnuts and a big orange drink anytime they wanted it.

Thin people have a long list of logical things they are always spouting off to me. They hold up one finger at a time as they reel off these things, so I won't lose track. They speak slowly as if to a young child. The list is long and full of holes. It contains tidbits like "get a grip on yourself," "cigarettes kill," "cholesterol clogs," "fit as a fiddle," "ducks in a row," "organize," and "sound fiscal management." Phrases like that.

They think these 2,000-point plans lead to happiness. Fat people know happiness is elusive at best and even if they could get the kind thin people talk about, they wouldn't want it. Wisely, fat people see that such programs are too dull, too hard, too off the mark. They are never better than a whole cheesecake.

Fat people know all about the mystery of life. They are the ones acquainted with the night, with luck, with fate, with playing it by ear. One thin person I know once suggested that we arrange all the parts of a jigsaw puzzle into groups according to size, shape, and color. He figured this would cut the time needed to complete the puzzle by at least 50 percent. I said I wouldn't do it. One, I like to muddle through. Two, what good would it do to finish early? Three, the jigsaw puzzle isn't the important thing. The important thing is the fun of four peo- 10 ple (one thin person included) sitting around a card table, working a jigsaw puzzle. My thin friend had no use for my list. Instead of join- 10 ing us, he went outside and mulched the boxwoods. The three re- maining fat people finished the puzzle and made chocolate, double-fudged brownies to celebrate.

10   The main problem with thin people is they oppress. Their good intentions, bony torsos, tight ships, neat corners, cerebral machina- tions, and pat solutions loom like dark clouds over the loose, com- fortable, spread-out, soft world of the fat. Long after fat people have removed their coats and shoes and put their feet up on the coffee table, thin people are still sitting on the edge of the sofa, looking neat as a pin, discussing rutabagas. Fat people are heavily into fits of laughter, slapping their thighs and whooping it up, while thin people are still politely waiting for the punch line.

Thin people are downers. They like math and morality and rea- soned evaluation of the limitations of human beings. They have their skinny little acts together. They expound, prognose, probe, and prick.

Fat people are convivial. They will like you even if you're irregu- lar and have acne. They will come up with a good reason why you never wrote the great American novel. They will cry in your beer with you. They will put your name in the pot. They will let you off the hook. Fat people will gab, giggle, guffaw, galumph, gyrate, and gossip. They are generous, giving, and gallant. They are gluttonous and goodly and great. What you want when you're down is soft and jiggly, not muscled and stable. Fat people know this. Fat people have plenty of room. Fat people will take you in.

The Digestive System and Nutrition

Colored SEM (× 20) of the lining of the stomach. The large folds flatten out when the stomach is full. The small indents are gastric pits.

Is "Overweight" Overstated?

If you have a body mass index (BMI) of greater than 25 but under 30, then you're officially considered overweight by the federal government. The government believes that your health may be at risk, and it's out to save you. You're likely to feel like you're being targeted by a concerted campaign to get you to eat better, exercise more, and above all, slim down! It's all very well meaning, of course, but there's a problem: Some of the statements made about the dangers of being overweight are based on poor science and weak statistics.

Several recent books have challenged the conventional wisdom that too much body fat is bad for your health. But they also have very little data to back up their claims—they're just telling us what we want to hear. It's time for a little scientific skepticism.

The hard fact is that nearly every scientific study conducted on the relationship between body fat and health risk has found a positive association between BMIs above the normal range and the risk of certain diseases. Those diseases include hypertension, type 2 diabetes, coronary heart disease, stroke, gallbladder disease, osteoarthritis, and several types of cancers. Being slightly overweight is *sometimes* a risk factor, but being obese generally *always* is.

The question becomes, then, "How much body fat is too much for *me*?" That's where the truth is unknown and misinformation begins. The answer depends on the specific disease you're concerned about and your lifestyle and genetic risk factors, not just on your BMI. To understand this, we need to understand the BMI scale; when it's useful and when it's not.

BMI and the Definition of "Overweight"

You and I tend to judge our fatness by getting on a bathroom scale. BMI is a bit

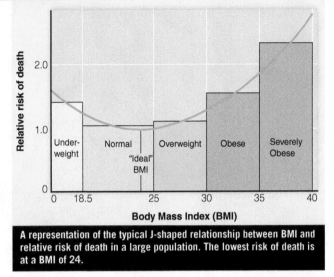

A representation of the typical J-shaped relationship between BMI and relative risk of death in a large population. The lowest risk of death is at a BMI of 24.

more precise because it takes height into account (see Figure 18). It is the simplest comparative measure of fatness. Its value is that it is easy to obtain, even as a self-report over the phone or on a questionnaire.

Before 1980 the BMI scale primarily was used by life insurance companies to predict mortality risk (risk of death). By then it was known that there's a normal, predictable U- or J-shaped relationship between risk of death and BMI (see graph), with people at the low and high ends of the scale at greater relative risk of dying in a given year.

It wasn't long before medical researchers began to use the BMI scale to look for the health risks associated with high BMIs within large populations. Literally hundreds of studies, some performed well and some not, came to the same conclusion—that especially at very high BMIs there is a positive relationship between BMI and certain chronic diseases.

But if that was true, shouldn't we be doing something about it? If only everyone were at that ideal BMI of 24, imagine all the lives that would be saved! It wasn't long before the government declared that women with a BMI over 27 and men with a BMI over 28 were officially "overweight," and

overweight was lumped with obesity as a health risk. A concerted educational campaign was begun to get us to eat better, exercise more often, and above all, lose that weight. The overzealous authors of one study even declared that "adults should try to maintain a BMI between 18.5 and 21.9 to minimize their risk of disease."

But the weight of the average U.S. adult kept rising, and government concern rose with it. In 1998 the federal government lowered its definition of overweight to include everyone over a BMI of 25. Overnight, another 29 million Americans were labeled overweight. And that's why by 2000, over 64% of the U.S. population was overweight or obese.

Overweight versus Obese— Different Levels of Risk

The first problem with any population-based definition of overweight is that it is not a good predictor of an individual's level of fitness or health. People who have a high muscle mass or who are just genetically built with larger body frames are likely to be labeled overweight or even obese by the BMI scale. The BMI may be a useful research tool for epidemiologists and public policymakers as they study whole populations, but it should not be used to make a recommendation about your personal lifestyle.

The second problem with the current definition of overweight is that it may have been oversold as a risk factor. Look again at the graph depicting mortality versus BMI. As a group, the overweight category has essentially no greater risk of dying than the

normal group. To be fair, a population with a BMI in the overweight range *is* at increased risk for some of those specific diseases listed above, such as diabetes, hypertension, and heart disease. But as you might expect, the risks are not as great

Daniel Berehulak/Getty Images

Regardless of her BMI, tennis champion Serena Williams would best be described as "fit."

as the risks associated with obesity or severe obesity. It's a matter of degree.

Is the government right to worry that obesity continues to rise in this country and to try to do something about it through public education? The answer is a resounding "yes." If every U.S. adult could somehow magically lose 10 pounds, would the incidence of hypertension, diabetes, and mortality go down? The answer again is "yes," but probably because it would reduce the number of obese or severely obese individuals, not because it would improve the health of people just barely overweight. If you've been labeled as overweight but you exercise regularly and eat properly, then lose 10 pounds if you want to, but don't do it because you think you'll live longer.

Questions to consider

1 Do you agree with the government's definition of overweight as BMIs above 25? Why or why not?

2 What do you think is government's proper role (if any) when it comes to noncommunicable health risks such as obesity?

The facts...

- According to government statistics, over 64% of the U.S. adult population is either overweight or obese.
- Statements about our national weight problem tend to lump overweight and obesity together as one problem.
- Obesity increases the risk of mortality and of certain chronic diseases. The health risk of being just slightly overweight is less severe.
- BMI is not particularly useful in assessing one's individual health.

The Chemistry of Living Things

Perennou Nuridsany/Photo Researchers, Inc.

Crystals of lactose, a carbohydrate. Human milk contains 6% lactose.

Functional Foods and Dietary Supplements—Safe and Effective?

Red Bull energy drink to boost our energy; glucosamine and chondroitin for our aching joints; extracts of *Ginkgo biloba* to improve our memories: We seem to have an appetite for functional foods and dietary supplements that promise to improve our health or make us feel better.

Functional foods, also sometimes called "nutraceuticals," are food or drink products that are said to have benefits beyond basic nutrition. Some are natural products; others are fortified foods or completely artificially created products. Red Bull is a functional food because of the manufacturer's claim that it "boosts

energy levels." Whole-wheat bread is a functional food, too, if the claim is made that the insoluble fiber in wheat bran "contributes to the maintenance of a healthy digestive tract."

Dietary supplements are products that are not normally part of the diet, but that you choose to take to improve your health or well-being. They include your daily multi-vitamin, as well as any supplemental minerals, amino acids, body-building products, plant extracts, and hormones you take by choice. Extracts of *Echinacea purpurea* taken to fight infections and extracts of *Ginkgo biloba* for improved memory are both dietary supplements.

Kristin Piljay

Do you know what's in this can?

Some natural-product dietary supplements, such as herbal remedies, have been around for hundreds or even thousands of years. Many of the ingredients in them probably do have specific health benefits. However, their effectiveness and safety in most cases have never been tested scientifically. How did this state of affairs come about, and are we comfortable with it? To understand this issue, it will help you to understand how and why functional foods and dietary supplements are regulated differently than pharmaceutical drugs (and why drugs cost so much!).

Regulatory Issues

The U.S. Food and Drug Administration (FDA) is responsible for overseeing the safety and efficacy of pharmaceutical drugs (drugs created specifically for the treatment or prevention of disease). By law, a pharmaceutical company must prove beyond a reasonable doubt that a new drug is safe and effective in humans before it can be sold to the public. On average it takes 12–15 years and costs about $800 million to bring one new drug to market. Companies can afford it only because they can patent the drug, giving them exclusive ownership and marketing rights for a certain number of years. Although patients sometimes complain about the high cost of prescription medications, pharmaceutical companies respond that the price reflects their steep development costs.

Because the ingredients in functional foods and dietary supplements occur in nature, they cannot be patented. Anyone can purify and package them. But without the assurance of patent protection, manufacturers and producers cannot afford to spend what it would cost to test their safety and effectiveness. Recognizing this, back in 1994 the dietary supplement manufacturers asked for (and were granted) an exemption from the FDA drug approval process. Under the Dietary Supplements Health and Education Act of 1994, dietary supplements and

functional foods can be produced and sold until they are *proven unsafe*. And why would any manufacturer choose to spend time and money to prove its own product unsafe? The FDA does not even need to be notified of "adverse events"; the agency must rely on voluntary information supplied by consumers and health professionals. As a result, the FDA reported only about 500 adverse events per year associated with dietary supplements over a five-year period. In contrast, the American Association of Poison Control Centers received nearly 7,000 reports involving dietary supplements in one year alone.

Producers and distributors of functional foods and dietary supplements also have considerable latitude in advertising their products; the only restriction is that they are not allowed to claim that their product prevents or treats specific medical conditions or diseases. For example, producers of cranberry juice products are free to say that cranberry juice "helps maintain urinary tract health" (a rather vague health claim), but they cannot claim that cranberry juice "prevents the recurrence of urinary tract infections" because that would represent a specific medical claim. Nevertheless, many consumers do use cranberry juice to treat urinary tract infections or to prevent their recurrence, simply because they believe that it works. And indeed it may; it's just that it has never been scientifically tested to the standards of a pharmaceutical drug.

With all that latitude in producing and marketing their products, it's not surprising that the functional foods and dietary supplements industries and the advertising industry that supports them have grown rapidly. U.S. sales of dietary supplements now top $18 billion a year.

Questions of Safety and Efficacy

Proponents of functional foods and dietary supplements argue that because many of these products have been in use for a long time, any adverse effects should have shown up by now. Critics argue that many

of the ingredients can now be synthesized chemically, and thus used at much higher concentrations and in different combinations than ever occur in nature. The active ingredients in Red Bull, for example, are all synthetically produced.

Cordelia Molloy/ Photo Researchers, Inc.

How will you determine if the supplement you're taking is safe and effective?

Other concerns include inaccurate product labeling and improper manufacturing processes. Manufacturers are not required to report quality control information to the FDA, so there is no assurance that the product actually contains what the manufacturer says it does. For example, independent tests found that products labeled as containing the same dosage of ginseng actually varied by a factor of 10 (some contained none at all). And California investigators found that nearly a third of all imported Asian herbal remedies they tested contained lead, arsenic, mercury, or drugs not mentioned on the label at all.

Consumers want to be assured that the dietary supplements and natural and fortified food products they use are safe. They'd like to know that the health claims about these products are true. How to achieve that goal and still ensure that the products remain available is an ongoing issue. In the meantime, it's up to you to know what is in the products you choose to put in your body.

Questions to consider

1 Who do you think should be responsible for ensuring that dietary supplements and functional foods are safe? Would you be willing to accept more regulation if it meant fewer products would be available? Explain your position.

2 What dietary supplements or functional foods do you use? Do you know what's in them and do you understand why you're using them?

The facts...

- **Functional foods and dietary supplements are popular with consumers. Americans consume more than $18 billion worth of dietary supplements every year.**

- **Functional foods and dietary supplements don't pass through the same rigorous approval procedure that is required of all new pharmaceutical drugs.**

- **Some products may not be effective; others may not be safe. However, increased regulation to ensure efficacy and safety would mean fewer products would be available.**

Whatsizface

David Rakoff

David Rakoff (1964–) was born in Montreal, Quebec, and grew up in Toronto. He is the youngest of three children. Both parents were M.D.s, his mother being a psychiatrist. He earned his B.A. (1986) from Columbia University in New York. He contributes essays to Public Radio's This American Life *and to the* New York Times Magazine. *He has worked in theater with good friends David and Amy Sedaris on their plays* Stitches, The Little Freida Mysteries, The Book of Liz, *and the Obie award-winning* One Woman Shoe. *He has published essays in* Vogue, Salon, The New York Observer, *and* Wired, *among others. He has twice received the Lambda Book Award for Humor, won the 2010 Academy Award for Best Live Action Short Film,* The New Tenants, *and appeared on* The Daily Show. *His books include* Don't Get Too Comfortable *(2005) and* Half Empty *(2010).*

1   I am not a handsome man. All that means is that my face has never been my fortune. Luckily for me, it hasn't been my punch line, either. I have some pretty eyes and, like everyone, I have my moments. I may even be thought attractive by those who love me, but that is emphatically not the same as the irrefutable mathematics of plane and placement that make for true beauty.

As a teenager reading *Death in Venice*, I understood the world to be divided between the Aschenbachs and the Tadzios. There are those who gaze, and those who are gazed upon. I am not talking about the natural inequity of attention that the old bestow upon the young— we are all hardwired to respond to babies, for example, but it would

---

take the rare and deeply odd child to singsong to a grown-up, "Who's got a cute receding hairline? Oh yes it is." I am talking about within one's own cohort: some are destined to promenade the Lido in Venice, blooming like flowers under the heat of appreciative stares, while the rest of us are born to watch, sweating through our grimy collars and eating our musty strawberries while the plague rolls in.

Inveterate Aschenbach that I have always been, we are at peace, my face and I, although it can be a tenuous cease-fire. A certain degree of dissatisfaction with my features is part of my cultural birthright. In my largely Jewish high school scores of girls got new noses for their birthdays, replacing their fantastic Litvak schnozes with "the Mindy," as Paul Rudnick has dubbed that shiny-skinned, characterless lump. Despite the prevalence and remarkable timing of these operations, coinciding as they so often did with upcoming Sweet Sixteens, they were always framed as life-or-death necessities— emergency procedures to repair lethally deviated septa and restore imperiled breathing. Even then, we knew enough to lie. Elective cosmetic surgery was the province of the irretrievably shallow. It was also a largely female pursuit. For most boys, failing the unlikely scenario wherein you infiltrated the mob, turned state's evidence, and got a new set of features thanks to the good doctors at the witness protection program, your face was an irreducible fact.

Still, without benefit of a mirror I can easily reel off all of the things I might change, given the opportunity. Starting at the top, they include a permanent red spot on the left side of my forehead; a brow pleated by worry: a furrow between my eyebrows so deep that at times it could be a coin slot; purple hollows underneath my eyes that I've had since infancy, and, also since childhood, lines like surveyors marks on my cheeks— placeholders for the inevitable eye bags I will have; a nose more fleshy and wide than prototypically Semitic, graced with a bouquet of tiny gin blossoms resulting from years of using neither sunscreen nor moisturizer; a set of those Fred Flintstone nasal creases down to the corners of my mouth; a permanent acne scar on my right cheek; a planklike expanse of filtrum between the bottom of my nose and the top of my too-thin upper lip; and, in profile, a double chin.

None of which is really a problem in New York City. Being a little goofy looking suits the supposed literary life-of-the-mind I lead here. (What a paper-thin lie. There are days when I'd throw out every book I own for the chance to be beautiful just once. Reading is hard, to paraphrase that discontinued Barbie.) Seriously contemplating the erasure or repair of any of these is inconceivable within the city limits. It's too small a town. There is a place, though, where the sunny notion of physical perfection and its achievement by any means necessary is carried unashamedly on the smoggy, orange-scented air: swimming pools, movie stars. Cue the banjo music.

I make consultations with two Beverly Hills surgeons. I want them to tell me what they might do, as though I had limitless inclination and resources, with no input from me. The reason for my silence is that I'd like outside confirmation of those things that are true flaws and those that are dysmorphic delusions on my part. There is also the vain hope that it is all dysmorphic delusion. That if I fail to bring it to their attention, somehow it will turn out that I've had the nose of a Greek statue all along. Primarily, though, I am hoping to catch them out in a moment of unchecked avarice; instead of proposing the unnecessary pinning back of my ears, I imagine them letting slip with their true purpose, as in, "I recommend the Italian ceramic back-splashes in my country house kitchen." Or "You'd look much better if my toxic punishing bitch of an ex-wife didn't insist on sending our eight-year-old daughter, Caitlin, to riding lessons in Malibu for $300 an hour."

Garth Fisher's practice is decorated with a grandeur disproportionate to the space, like a studio apartment tricked out with pieces from the set of *Intolerance*. The waiting area has overstuffed sofas, a small flat-screen TV in the corner, tasseled wall sconces, and a domed oculus in the low ceiling, painted with clouds. Fisher's office is full of bulky antique furniture in dark wood with turned legs, armoires, walnut book-cases. Behind his desk are many photographs of his wife, Brooke Burke, a model and television personality. Were I differently placed on the Kinsey scale, I might even pronounce her "hot," dropping my voice an octave and adding an extra syllable to the word. She is a near-perfect beauty.

   Fisher himself is also nice-looking, a handsome man in his early forties. Blue-eyed and chestnut-haired, he has a bit of the early-seventies Aqua Velva hunk about him. I ask him, looking directly at the enviable cleft in his chin, if he's had any work done himself. Very little. A tiny bit of botox between his brows and some veneers on his teeth. He also had his nose done, to correct some football injuries. To my dismay, he is similarly conservative in his approach to others. Of the eight potential patients he saw that day, he refused to take on seven of them. Some were not candidates while others had unreasonable expectations about what plastic surgery can realistically do, even now.

"This is the Dark Ages. This is like 1904," he says. Future generations will be amazed by the inevitable advances, he predicts. For now he is more than willing to allow other doctors to use their patient populations as the guinea pigs for new and experimental treatments. He has not done a penile augmentation, for example ("scary business"), neither does he offer those silicone pectoral or calf implants.

10 "I want a simple life. All I've got to do is do a good job and tell 10 the truth."

The only reason he agrees to give me unsolicited advice is that he knows I am a writer (indeed, the only way I could get an appointment with two top Beverly Hills plastic surgeons is that they know I am a writer). He remains notably uncomfortable with the charade. "If someone comes in here like this," he pulls his ears out from his head like Dumbo, "and all they want fixed is the mole on their chin, then that's all I'm going to mention." Assured of my thick skin, he eventually allows as how he might "clean some things up" that steal focus from my eyes.

We go into an examining room where he keeps his computer simulator. The process begins with taking two photographs—the "befores." I look the way I always do, but it's embarrassing to see myself up on the monitor with another person sitting there. My profile looks careworn, simultaneously bald and hairy. My eyes are sunk into craters of liver-colored flesh, and my ear is a greasy nautilus, as if I'd just come from listening to a deep-fat fryer.

Fisher demonstrates his morphing tool by drawing a circle around my chin with the mouse. Pulling the cursor, he extends my jaw out like a croissant. It is a fabulous toy. I want to wrest the mouse from his control and really go to town, giving myself fleshy horns, pointy corkscrew ears. If he would only let me, I would pull out the flanges of my nostrils until they looked like the wings of Eero Saarinen's TWA terminal at JFK. "But your chin is perfect," he says, snapping it and me back to reality. "Three millimeters behind your bottom lip." Instead, he points out how the end of my nose droops down to the floor, while the arch of my nostrils is very high. (I write "too high" in my notebook before realizing that these are my words, not his.) He raises the tip, lowers my nostrils, and then straightens out the slope of the nose itself. It is subtle and aquiline. He then smoothes out the area under my eyes. In real life this would involve the removal of some fat and tightening up the skin. Finally, he points to the small vertical indentation between my brows, just like the one he had before botox. He recommends a small amount of the neurotoxin, just enough to smooth it out without robbing me of my capacity to emote. Of all the features that render me less than perfect, I've actually always sort of been attached to those that lend me an air of gravitas, covering up my shortcomings of character and intellect. I ask if it's all right to leave it as is. "Well," he shrugs, "it's okay if you're playing a lawyer or a judge." Instead, I get him to give me a slight Mick Jagger moue. "I don't like those lips, but I'll let you have them." He plumps up my mouth.

The photographs are printed out, the two images side by side against a dark background with no discernible seam between them. I am a set of twins. My original self seems a melancholic killjoy. His reengineered brother, on the other hand, looks clean and a little haughty. And how about that marvelous new nose! Pointy, sharp, a weapon. Despite that old stereotype about Jewish intellectual superiority, I think I appear cleverer as well ("perspicacious," as my ethnically cleansed self might say). Fisher's instinct about my new mouth was also right on the money. It gives me the beginnings of a snarl, like I've wedged a handful of Tic Tacs in front of my upper teeth.

15. But even my misbegotten new upper lip cannot dampen my spirits. I step out into the beautiful California dusk to catch a cab with a spring in my step. I'm feeling handsome, as though Fisher's changes were already manifest on my face and not just in the envelope of photographs I clutch. Reality soon sets in. The sidewalk of Santa Monica Boulevard simply ends without warning and I have to dart, terrified, across four lanes of traffic. I cannot find a taxi on the deserted leafy streets of Beverly Hills, and I have to walk all the way back to my hotel. "Good evening," the beautiful young doorman says to me when I arrive, an hour and a half later. He smiles in my direction, but his eyes are looking just above my left ear.

Studying the photographs the next morning, I am already experiencing some misgivings. It is not the regret of "What have I done?" that dogs me so much as a feeling that I want more. I briefly curse Garth Fisher's innate professionalism and hope that Richard Ellenbogen, my next surgeon, will not hang back and keep me from achieving my true physical glory.

If his office is any indication, I'm in luck. Where Fisher's was the McMansion version of the baths at Pompeii, Richard Ellenbogen's Sunset Boulevard practice (hard by the Hamburger Hamlet where Dean Martin ate every day) defies easy aesthetic description. It is an astonishment of styles and motifs. The reception desk is framed by two arching female figureheads as might be found on the prow of a Spanish galleon. The walls of the waiting room are peach plaster set with Tudor timbers. There is an ornamental brick fireplace in the corner, sofas in floral chintz, and everywhere, absolutely everywhere—on the mantel, along the plate rail (hung with swags of floral chintz bunting)—are ormolu clocks, Bakelite and old wooden radios, commemorative plates, lamps and small sculptures of those young, barely pubescent deco-era girls, the kind who festoon old movie-palace plaster and frequently hold aloft globe lights. All of it in under 150 square feet.

There is a benevolence to this crowded exuberance; one's own physical flaws shrink to nothing in the midst of such riotous excess. The staff is friendly and funny. "Here to get your breasts done?" cracks one woman when she sees me. Another confides, "Sometimes he," meaning Ellenbogen, "will just say to a patient, 'You don't need this. Buy a new dress and save your money.' We love our patients."

Ellenbogen is known for fat grafting and facial reshaping. Instead of pulling and tightening a face, he replaces the fat in the areas that used to be fuller, before aging and gravity did their work. For a patient in their mid-fifties, for example, he will analyze a photograph of them at half that age and isolate the facial regions in need of filling. The patients I look at in his albums do seem *juicy*, for lack of a better word, although the result looks not so much younger as vegetal. They look like Arcimboldo paintings, those Renaissance portraits constructed entirely out of fruit. To give them their due, they don't look like drum-tight gorgons, either. In folder after folder, I do not come across even one of those monstrous surgerized analogues of Joan Rivers. Where are those faces, I wonder aloud to Ellenbogen?

20 "We call that the New York look," he says. Apparently, there is 20 less need for that kind of wholesale renovation in Los Angeles, where Hollywood hopefuls have been a self-selecting group for almost a century. "People are prettier here. It's now the children and grandchildren of Sandra Dee. In New York, you've still got all those great Jewish immigrant faces." Ellenbogen is allowed to say this, possessed of one as he is himself. (He's had some botox, his neck done, and lipo on his

love handles, although he still supports a somewhat cantilevered belly as befits a man of sixty.)

He doesn't do computer imaging. "It's hokey. It's used by people who aren't artists. It's not a true representation of what a surgeon can actually do. It's like a real estate agent saying, 'This would be such an incredible view if you just planted some trees here and put in a garden . . .'" Instead, he takes two Polaroids and, using a small brush, mixes together unbleached titanium and burnt umber and paints the changes on one of them. Like Fisher, even with carte blanche, Ellenbogen only envisions minor treatments. Again with the straightening of the nose and raising the tip (one hour), he would also build out my chin a little bit, using a narrow curving strip of milky white silicone—like something from the toe of a high-end running shoe—fed down through the mouth behind the lower lip (ten minutes), and a final procedure (fifteen minutes) in which he would inject fat into my extremely deep nasojugal folds, those tear troughs under my eyes. (Garth Fisher is not a fan of regrafting. "You'd love your doctor for six months," and no longer, he implies.) Total cost, around $12,000.

There is nothing so intimately known as our own face. Even the most deprived existence provides opportunities to gaze into a reflective surface now and then—puddles of standing water, soup spoons, the sides of toasters. We know what pleases us, and also have a fairly good sense of what we would change if we could. Sometimes, though, we just get it plain wrong. Ellenbogen shows me a photo of a young man in his twenties; a pale, strawberry blond with the kind of meek profile that gets shoved into lockers. "This kid came in and wanted me to fix his nose. 'It's too big!' he said. I told him, 'It's not your nose. I'll prove it to you. I'll build out your chin. If you don't like it, I'll take it out and do your nose for free.' " Ellenbogen was right. The merest moving forward of the jaw has made the nose recede. The change is remarkable.

The fellow may have been focusing on the wrong feature, but at least he wanted *something*. There is a reason that both Fisher and Ellenbogen were so reluctant to suggest procedures to me. An unspecified and overarching desire for change speaks to a dissatisfaction probably better served by a psychiatrist. One surgeon I spoke to will not treat people in their first year of widowhood for just that reason. To briefly rant about *The Swan*, the television show that takes depressed female contestants—all of whom seem to need little more than to change out of their sweat suits and get some therapy—and makes them all over to look like the same trannie hooker: what makes *The Swan* truly vile is that for the months that these women are being carved up like so much processed poultry, all of the mirrors in their lives are covered over. Such willing abrogation of any say or agency in how they will be transformed *by definition* means that in the real world, they would not be candidates for surgery. It is the very sleaziest of all the plastic-surgery makeover shows—quite a distinction, that; like being voted the Osbourne child with the fewest interests.

Garth Fisher, in what might be considered an unconscious act of penance for contributing to the culture in which something like *The Swan* can exist (he is the in-house surgeon for the comparatively classier *Extreme Makeover*), has created a five-hour DVD series called *The Naked Truth About Plastic Surgery*. Each hour-long disk is devoted to a different procedure and region of the body—breast augmentation, brow lifts, etc.

25   In spirit, *The Naked Truth* is more educational tool than sales   25 pitch. It is refreshingly up front about the complications that can arise, like bad scarring, hematoma, numbness, pigment irregularities, infection, skin loss, even embolism and death. In the liposuction section, there is a shot of Fisher in the operating room. The backs of the patient's legs are shiny brown from the pre-surgical iodine wash, and crisscrossed with felt-tip marker. Fisher is sawing away under the shuddering skin with the cannula, a tool resembling a sharp, narrow pennywhistle attached to a hose. There is a savagery to his movements, the way one might angrily go back and forth over a particularly tenacious piece of lint with a vacuum cleaner. He looks up at the camera, his arm going the whole time. Although wearing a mask, his eyes crinkle in an unmistakable "Well, hello there!" smile.

There are shots of clear plastic containers of extracted fat—frothy, orange-yellow foam floating atop a layer of dark blood—and pictures of postoperative faces looking like Marlon Brando after he's been worked over in *On the Waterfront*. Such footage might have once had a deterrent effect but is now familiar to any toddler who has ever been parked in front of The Learning Channel. That these images have to be followed up by the cautionary tone of a narrator who says, "just because something *can* be done does not mean it *should* be done" and "if you can reach your goal without surgery, then you are better off," speaks to how far down the rabbit hole we've tumbled. It's as if the whole country regularly watched newsreel footage of buses full of children going off of cliffs and was still blithely picking up the phone to make bookings with Greyhound.

I might be more apt to drink the Kool-Aid if I was more impressed by the results. The before and after photos of liposuction, for example, do show a reduction in volume. But if I were to endure the risks of general anesthetic, the pain, the constriction garment that must be worn like a sausage casing for weeks after the surgery, and the months-long wait for final results, I wouldn't just want a flatter stomach with no trace of love handles. I would insist upon the tortoiseshell reticulation of a six-pack, that abdominal Holy Grail. That's hard to achieve with liposuction. There is a procedure that replicates the look, called "etching," where the coveted tic-tac-toe pattern is suctioned out of the adipose tissue, giving the appearance of musculature with no muscles present; morphology absent of structure, like the false bones in McDonald's creepy McRib sandwich. Garth Fisher doesn't recommend or offer it. Gain weight, he points out, and the artificially differentiated lobes of your fat expand and rise from your stomach like a pan of buttermilk biscuits.

In the end, it is neither thrift nor fear of the knife that deters me. Far more than the physical transformation, it would be the very decision to go ahead with it that would render me unrecognizable to myself.

I once bleached my hair almost to platinum for a part in a short film. It lent me a certain Teutonic unapproachability, which I liked. But as it grew out, it faded to an acid, Marshmallow Peep yellow and my head started to look like a drugstore Easter-promotion window. Dark roots and straw-dry hair look fine on a college kid experimenting with peroxide, but I looked like a man of a certain age with a bad dye job clutching at his fleeting youth with bloody fingernails. I could see pity in the faces of strangers who passed me on the street. *Mutton dressed as lamb*, they were thinking. To all the world, I was the guy who broadcasts that heartbreaking and ambivalent directive: "Look at me, but for the reasons you used to!"

30 It must be murder to be an aging beauty, a former Tadzio, to see 30 your future as an ignored spectator rushing up to meet you like the hard pavement. What a small sip of gall to be able to time with each passing year the ever-shorter interval in which someone's eyes focus upon you. And then shift away.

Steroid Report Cites 'Collective Failure'

Duff Wilson and Michael S. Schmidt

Duff Wilson was born in 1953. He graduated from Western Washington University in 1976 and received a masters degree from the Columbia University Graduate School of Journalism in 1982. He became an investigative projects director for the Seattle Times *in 1989 and a sports-related investigative reporter for* The New York Times *in 2004. Previously he had worked for the Associated Press and the* Seattle Post-Intelligencer. *Duff serves the Investigative Reporters and Editors, a non-profit group dedicated to improving the quality of investigative journalism, as a member of the First Amendment Committee. He has twice been awarded the Harvard University Goldsmith Prize for Investigative Reporting and twice won the George Polk Award. He is a recipient of the Loeb Award given by UCLA's Anderson School of Management and on three occasions was a finalist for the Pulitzer Prize, among many other prizes and distinctions. Two of his most important co-authored articles are "Suddenly Sick," which exposed corruption in the pharmaceutical industry, and "Uniformed Consent," dealing with conflicts of interest at the Fred Hutchinson Cancer Center in Seattle. Duff is the author of* Fateful Harvest: The True Story of a Small Town, a Global Industry, and a Toxic Secret *(2001), about the mayor of a small Washington State community who exposed corrupt hazardous waste disposal practices. It was based on an earlier investigative report titled "Fear in the Fields: How Hazardous Wastes Become Fertilizer," and was awarded book-of-the Year honors from Investigative*

Reporters and Editors. The following selection, which Duff co-authored with Michael S. Schmidt also of the Times, *offers an account of the George Mitchell report exposing steroid use in professional baseball.*

1   Former Senator *George J. Mitchell* released a blistering report Thursday that tied 89 Major League Baseball players, including *Roger Clemens*, to the use of illegal, performance-enhancing drugs. The report used informant testimony and supporting documents to provide a richly detailed portrait of what Mr. Mitchell described as "baseball's steroids era."

Mr. Clemens, a seven-time Cy Young Award winner, was the most prominent name on a list that included seven other former most valuable players as well as players from all 30 teams. The list included more than a dozen players who have had significant roles with the *Yankees*, and more than a dozen *Mets*, too. It also included 11 players alone from the 2000 *Los Angeles Dodgers*.

Of all the active players tied to the use of steroids and human growth hormone, which are illegal without a prescription and banned by baseball, only *Jason Giambi* of the Yankees cooperated with Mitchell's 20-month investigation. The *Toronto Blue Jays'* Frank Thomas, widely known for his antisteroids stance, was the only other active player who agreed to talk with Mr. Mitchell's investigators.

Mr. Mitchell's report of about 400 pages was based on interviews with more than 700 people, including 60 former players, and 115,000 pages of documents, including receipts, canceled checks, telephone records and e-mail messages. The key evidence was provided by Kirk Radomski, a former Mets clubhouse attendant, and Brian McNamee, a former trainer for Mr. Clemens and Yankees pitcher *Andy Pettitte,* who was also named in the report.

5   In the report, Mr. McNamee is quoted describing how he injected Mr. Clemens with illegal drugs at least 16 times from 1998 through 2001. Mr. Clemens, 45, adamantly denied the report's accusations of his use of steroids and human growth hormone, his Houston lawyer, *Rusty Hardin*, said in a telephone interview Thursday night. Mr. Hardin said he had been told Mr. McNamee was pressured to give up names or face prosecution by the I.R.S. Special Agent Jeff Novitzky, who has led the *Bay Area Laboratory Co-Operative* and Radomski investigations.

Mr. Hardin criticized Mr. Mitchell for naming players based on uncorroborated allegations. "He has thrown a skunk into the jury box, and we will never be able to remove that smell," Mr. Hardin said. Mr. Pettitte's agent declined to comment.

In his comments at a Midtown Manhattan hotel Thursday, Mr. Mitchell acknowledged that his report was inhibited by limited cooperation and the absence of subpoena power, and that there was still much about drug use in baseball he did not know. The report was critical of the commissioner's office and the players' union for knowingly tolerating performance-enhancing drugs. It cited many instances where club officials knew about particular steroid use among players and did not report it.

"There was a collective failure to recognize the problem as it emerged and to deal with it early on," Mr. Mitchell said. He recommended that the players on the list not be disciplined, but instead said that baseball needed to "look ahead to the future" and establish stronger testing.

Bud Selig, the commissioner of baseball, praised Mr. Mitchell's 20 recommendations, which included the adoption of a more independent drug-testing program with more public reporting of results, and the establishment of a unit in the commissioner's office to investigate reports of steroid use by players who have not tested positive.

10 Despite Mr. Mitchell's general recommendation that the players in the report not be punished, Mr. Selig said he would review each player's case individually and was inclined to discipline them. 10

"His report is a call to action," Mr. Selig said. "And I will act."

Donald M. Fehr, the executive director of the Major League Players' Association, said he did not think the investigation was fair.

"Many players are named," Mr. Fehr said. "Their reputations have been adversely affected, probably forever, even if it turns out down the road that they should not have been."

Mr. Mitchell said "baseball's steroids era" started roughly in 1988. It took 15 more years for baseball to start random testing, Mr. Mitchell said. He noted that testing has reduced steroid usage, but players have switched to human growth hormone, which cannot be detected in urine tests, which baseball's program administers. "Everybody in baseball—commissioners, club officials, the players' association, players—shares responsibility," Mr. Mitchell said.

15   The report revealed that baseball secretly suspended drug testing for 15 part of the 2004 season, for fear of criminal prosecution, after federal authorities seized the 2003 drug results as part of the Balco case. The suspension, of unclear length, was kept secret by agreement of the commissioner's office and the players' association.

Mr. McNamee, who has also been employed as a trainer with the Yankees and the Toronto Blue Jays, spoke to Mr. Mitchell's investigators under pressure from federal prosecutors investigating the use of steroids in baseball. Mr. McNamee, who was linked with Mr. Radomski, provided evidence against Mr. Clemens, Mr. Pettitte and first baseman David Segui. Mr. McNamee agreed to cooperate with the United States Attorney's Office under the terms that he would not be charged with a crime if he told Mr. Mitchell and investigators the truth.

The report was littered with vivid details, including Mr. Radomski telling investigators that he once found on his porch a wet delivery package filled with $8,000 in cash from *Kevin Brown*, the former Dodgers and Yankees pitcher.

Mitchell's report described how *David Justice* denied using steroids to investigators while providing names of players that he suspected of using them. Justice, a former Yankees and *Atlanta Braves* outfielder, is among the players named in the report.

A Congressional committee that held a televised hearing on steroids in baseball in 2005 called another hearing for next Tuesday and summoned Mr. Mitchell, Mr. Selig and Mr. Fehr.

20   Mr. Radomski, who has pleaded guilty to federal charges for sell- 20 ing steroids from 1995 through 2005, cooperated with Mr. Mitchell as part of his plea bargain. He is to be sentenced next year on federal charges of steroid distribution.

Other evidence came from Mr. McNamee, and from an investigation led by the Albany County district attorney into Signature Pharmacy. "The players' union was largely uncooperative for reasons which I think were understandable," Mr. Mitchell said.

The report described case after case where players were caught with steroids but not pursued by club officials or the commissioner's security office.

The report listed key members of the Yankees' World Series teams in the *Joe Torre* era, including starting pitchers Clemens and the 35-year-old Pettitte, the left-handed and right-handed set-up men

Mike Stanton and Jason Grimsley, right fielder Justice and second baseman *Chuck Knoblauch*.

Mr. Selig said baseball would immediately cease giving teams advance notice of when drug testers would be showing up. The testers had been calling clubs the day before testing to get parking passes at ballparks. That practice was revealed recently by The New York Times.

25 "For more than a decade, there has been widespread anabolic steroid use," Mr. Mitchell said. He said the use of performance-enhancing substances "poses a serious threat to the integrity of the game." 25

The other prominent names in the report were the Most Valuable Player award-winners *Barry Bonds*, *Ken Caminiti*, José Canseco, Giambi, Juan González, *Mo Vaughn* and Miguel Tejada.

Other players named included *Gary Sheffield*, Lenny Dykstra, *Denny Neagle*, *Todd Hundley*, Mike Stanton, Paul Lo Duca and Eric Gagné.

Don Hooton, who became an outspoken critic of steroid use after his son Taylor committed suicide after using the drugs, attended the news conference Thursday and said of the report, "This is more than about asterisks and cheating; it's about the lives and health of our kids."

Mr. Selig noted that he had the authority to implement several of the recommendations, but that the majority—including any changes to the sport's drug-testing policies—would first have to be agreed to by the players' association under the terms of the collective-bargaining agreement. Mr. Fehr said the union would be willing to take a look at the possibility of adjusting the testing procedures before the agreement expires in 2011. Mr. Mitchell's report did not address the use of amphetamines in sports, nor did it call for blood testing, the only way to detect human growth hormone.

30 "Former commissioner *Fay Vincent* told me that the problem of performance-enhancing substances may be the most serious challenge that baseball has faced since the 1919 Black Sox scandal," Mr. Mitchell said in the report, referring to the *Chicago White Sox'* throwing of the World Series. 30

Mr. Mitchell has conducted the reported $20 million investigation with the help of his law firm DLA Piper, where he is a partner. Mr. Mitchell has made few public statements throughout the investigation and many of the details have been guarded.

He serves as a director of the *Red Sox*, a post he refused to vacate despite accusations that his investigation might be biased toward the team.

Mr. Mitchell had a difficult time with the players' union.

"The Players' Association was largely uncooperative," Mr. Mitchell wrote, discouraging every active baseball player from talking with him, rejecting all requests for documents, and permitting only one interview with Mr. Fehr.

The Muscular System

John Burcham/National Geographic Creative/Getty Images

Climber in Banff National Park, Canada.

Drug Abuse Among Athletes

Baseball slugger Barry Bonds is under indictment for lying under oath about using performance-enhancing drugs. Sprinter Marion Jones confessed to her drug use and offered a tearful apology, but was stripped of her five Olympic gold medals. High school athletes are routinely being tested for performance-enhancing drugs. What is going on here?

The short answer is that many performance-enhancing drugs do enhance athletic performance. They work in ways that are predictable and understood, based on human physiology. In an environment where just a hundredth of a second can make the

difference between an Olympic gold medal and relative obscurity, the temptation to use these drugs is high.

Anabolic Steroids

Anabolic steroids and related compounds such as dehydroepiandrosterone (DHEA) and androstenedione ("Andro") are the most widely abused drugs in athletics today. Although anabolic steroids are banned by sports federations and school systems, many of them are available over the counter as the result of a 1994 federal law that was written to ensure access to herbal remedies. In general, they are

Scott Barbour/Getty Images

Hiroko Masuike/Getty Images

Marion Jones after winning the gold in 2000, and in 2007 after admitting to using performance-enhancing drugs.

structurally and functionally related to the male sex steroid testosterone. And like testosterone, they make it easy for the user to increase his/her muscle mass. Muscle strength improves as well, leading to improved athletic performance in sports that require short bursts of energy.

How common is anabolic steroid use? A study funded by the National Institute on Drug Abuse found that 2.5% of 12th-graders, 1.5% of 10th-graders and 1.1% of 8th-graders had tried them. Information on steroid use by college and professional athletes is unreliable because the athletes are reluctant to talk about it. A few well-known athletes, including Arnold Schwarzenegger, sprinter Ben Johnson, and wrestler Hulk Hogan, have admitted to using them at one time or another.

A recent trend is the increased use of sophisticated "designer drugs" such as THG (tetrahydrogestrinone), designed specifically to avoid detection. THG is known as "the clear" to athletes because allegedly it couldn't be detected. And for years it wasn't detected—until an anonymous tipster sent a sample of the drug to a sport federation for testing. THG is so potent that it doesn't even have to be injected—just a couple of drops under the tongue are enough. In 2007 sprinter Marion Jones finally admitted that she started using THG in 1999 as she prepared for the 2000 Olympic games. She was stripped of her five medals from the 2000 Olympics and banned from participation in the 2008 Olympics in Beijing.

Aside from the obvious issue of fairness in athletic competition, anabolic steroids are banned by sports federations because of their side effects and possible health risks. Androgens have masculinizing effects in both sexes. Men may experience gynecomastia (enlargement of the breasts), shrinkage of the testicles, reduced sperm production, and impotence. In women, breast size and body fat decrease and the voice deepens. Women may lose scalp hair but gain body hair. Some of these changes

A young Barry Bonds playing for the Pirates, and years later, a bulkier Barry as the SF Giants' slugger.

Hiroko Masuike/Getty Images

Dilip Vishwana/Getty Images

are not reversible. Anabolic steroid abuse is also associated with irritability, hostility, and aggressive behavior ("roid rage"). Prolonged anabolic steroid abuse is associated with an increased risk of heart attack, stroke, and severe liver disease, including liver cancer. Although the number of cases of these diseases is fairly low (so far), the effects of steroid use/abuse may be underestimated because these diseases tend to come later in life. We just don't know what will happen to steroid abusers 30 years later.

Blood Enhancers

Marathoners and cyclists aren't interested in muscle mass; they're interested in maintaining a high level of sustained performance over long periods of time. For that, they need increased aerobic capacity. Their (banned) drug of choice is erythropoietin (EPO), a hormone produced by the kidneys that increases the production of red blood cells. EPO is available by prescription only for patients with *anemia* (too few red blood cells in the blood). But cyclists and marathon runners use it to improve their performance. It's all a matter of normal human physiology; EPO produces more red blood cells, which leads to a higher oxygen-carrying capacity, which in turn leads to a higher level of sustainable muscle activity and faster times.

But a health risk is associated with EPO abuse. Excessive production of red blood cells can raise the hematocrit (the percentage of the blood that is red cells) to dangerous levels. The blood becomes sludge-like, increasing the risk of high blood pressure, blood clots, and heart attacks. Statistically, one of the most common causes of death among professional cyclists is heart attack, although no deaths have ever officially been listed as having been caused by EPO.

It's hard to test for EPO abuse because EPO disappears from the blood within days, leaving behind an increased hematocrit and an improved endurance that lasts for a month or more. The cycling organizations are only able to curb EPO abuse by setting an upper limit for hematocrit of 50%; above that, EPO abuse is just assumed and the athlete is banned from competition. It is widely suspected that cyclists who choose to abuse EPO measure their hematocrit shortly before a race and then remove blood cells to just meet the 50% rule!

Next Up: Gene Doping

Within decades, it will probably be possible to use genetic engineering techniques to modify an athlete's genes for improved athletic performance. It's called *gene doping*. What if you could tinker with the genes that lead to the production of natural erythropoietin or testosterone, so that an athlete just naturally produces more of these hormones? What if you could alter muscle biochemistry so that muscles used energy more efficiently or more rapidly? What if you could insert genes that caused muscle cells to store up more ATP? These ideas are not so far-fetched. Nearly all experts on the subject are convinced that if gene doping hasn't been tried already, it soon will be. Gene doping will be extremely hard to detect or to prevent.

Have we lost our perspective for the role that sports should play in our lives?

Questions to consider

1 Do you think we should continue to try to prevent the use of drugs and genetic engineering in sports? Why or why not?

2 A friend who uses anabolic steroids says that there is no convincing scientific evidence that anabolic steroid use will lead to health problems such as heart disease or cancer later in life. Is he right? What would you say to him?

The facts...

- Performance-enhancing drugs such as anabolic steroids and erythropoietin (EPO) are used by some athletes because they improve certain types of athletic performance.
- Abuse of performance-enhancing drugs can lead to unwanted side effects, an increased risk of certain chronic diseases, and perhaps even premature death.
- Although most sports federations have banned the use of performance-enhancing drugs, enforcement has proven difficult.
- Soon it may be possible to use genetic engineering techniques to enhance athletic performance.

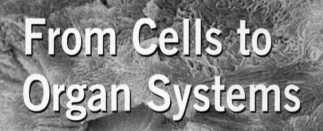

From Cells to Organ Systems

Steve Gschmeissner/Photo Researchers

Dried skin cells on the surface of the skin.

Can Lipodissolve Melt Away Fat?

When you are familiar with the chemistry of lipids and the structure and function of fat cells, you understand that when your average daily caloric intake exceeds your average daily caloric expenditure, you gain weight. And yet all this knowledge hasn't helped, because you still have those annoying fat deposits in places where you don't want them! Perhaps you've tried dieting and exercise and still aren't happy with your body shape.

What if you could just melt away that unwanted fat? What if you could kill some of those pesky fat cells once and for all? What if you could sculpt your body into perfect shape without ever having to diet or exercise again? It's a fantasy many of us have indulged in, and it's one of the reasons for the meteoric rise of a controversial cosmetic procedure called *Lipodissolve*.

What Is Lipodissolve?

Lipodissolve, also called injection lipolysis, is described by its promoters as a safe, effective, nonsurgical way to sculpt the body into perfect shape. Usually the technique is performed as a series of six injections two weeks apart directly into

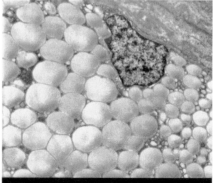

Liu Jin/Getty Images

A human fat cell (× 3,000) filled with lipid droplets (yellow).

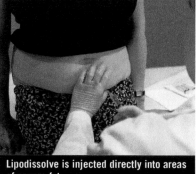

Lipodissolve is injected directly into areas of excess fat.

subcutaneous fat deposits. The injections contain two active ingredients: phosphatidylcholine (a phospholipid) and deoxycholate (a bile acid). The combination of these two drugs, known as PCDC (for phosphotidylcholine deoxycholate), allegedly works by dissolving the bonds between the three fatty acids and the glycerol backbone that comprise a triglyceride molecule, the primary molecular form of stored fat in the body. PCDC also is thought to disrupt the cell membranes of fat cells in the vicinity of an injection, resulting in death of the fat cells themselves. Some Lipodissolve cocktails also include vitamins and plant extracts.

And at the moment, the safety and effectiveness of Lipodissolve are not backed by scientific data. The Food and Drug Administration (FDA) has called Lipodissolve just another example of "unapproved drugs for unapproved uses." Nevertheless Lipodissolve clinics can legally administer Lipodissolve because of a loophole in our drug regulatory laws. According to the law, a licensed doctor can legally and ethically prescribe compounded drugs (drugs made from more than one ingredient) specifically for individual patients, as long as all of the *ingredients* are approved by the FDA. The intent is to protect the sanctity of the doctor/patient relationship, allowing the doctor to choose what is best for that particular patient. Both of the compounds in a Lipodissolve injection have been approved by the FDA as ingredients in other drugs,

though neither was approved as a fat-dissolving drug.

Health clinics and spas have been quick to capitalize on the loophole, for at prices ranging from $400 to $1,500 per Lipodissolve treatment they stand to make a lot of money. Most patients who try the technique eventually sign up for treatment of several body parts. Women generally request treatment of their thighs and abdomen, whereas men are more likely to choose jaw lines and love handles. One of the distinct advantages of the technique is that because it does not involve surgery there is no recovery period. Not surprisingly, there are persistent rumors on various celebrity-watch Web sites that certain celebrities have tried the procedure or are thinking about it.

One of the first companies to offer the Lipodissolve technique in this country was Advanced LipoDissolve Center, later renamed fig. (short for figure). Fig.'s "dissolve to your beautiful shape" advertising campaign was so successful that the company grew to 18 body-shaping centers in eight states in just two years. The company went out of business in late 2007, but there are still plenty of other clinics and spas willing to perform the Lipodissolve procedure.

Is Lipodissolve Safe and Effective?

Critics of the Lipodissolve technique argue that the current law covering single doctor/patient relationships was never intended to allow mass marketing by chains of clinics or spas, or mass compounding of the PCDC drug combination. The American Society of Plastic Surgeons, The American Society of Aesthetic Plastic Surgery, and the American Society of Dermatologic Surgery have issued cautionary warnings against the technique, but that's understandable since all three societies represent surgeons who might be financially affected by Lipodissolve's increasing popularity. Lipodissolve proponents, on the other hand, counter by pointing out that there have been only anecdotal reports of minor unwanted side effects

associated with the technique, such as swelling, skin blistering, pain, and blackened skin in some patients. No deaths have been reported. However, because the technique has been performed in this country only since 2004, the long-term consequences of Lipodissolve therapy are still unknown. Some scientists worry that disruption of fat cell membranes at the site of injection might cause a sharp rise in cholesterol in the blood. After all, cholesterol is a normal constituent of cell membranes. In addition, little is known about how the Lipodissolve drugs are metabolized or removed from the body. Nor is it known whether they enter the circulatory system in sufficient quantities to affect other organs or tissues far from the injection site.

Does Lipodissolve work? The jury is still out on this one. Some patients see an improvement in body shape after Lipodissolve, others do not. One possible reason for differences in effectiveness between patients may be that there is no standard dose of Lipodissolve. The procedure is not regulated by the FDA, so physicians are free to try any combination of doses, injection intervals, and treatment sites they want.

Faced with the awkward and potentially dangerous situation of having patients flock to an unregulated procedure, the FDA decided to take action. Late in 2007 the FDA approved the first clinical trial of Lipodissolve—a double-blind, placebo-controlled prospective study that will follow patients for up to 46 weeks. The trial, to be conducted by the research arm of the American Society for Aesthetic Plastic Surgery, is expected to provide the first scientifically defensible data on the efficacy and safety of Lipodissolve. The results may not be known for several more years. In the meantime the FDA is keeping an eye on the situation. Consumers would be wise to remain skeptical about this procedure until more is known about it.

Questions to consider

1 Health clinics sometimes cite retrospective studies to support their claim that the Lipodissolve technique is safe. What is a "retrospective study"? How is it different from a controlled study?

2 How important is FDA approval and/or scientific evidence of safety to you? If someone were to pay for a Lipodissolve procedure for you, would you try it?

The facts...

- A nonsurgical cosmetic procedure for "melting away fat" is being heavily promoted by health clinics and spas.

- The procedure, called *Lipodissolve*, involves a series of injections of fat-dissolving drugs directly into local fat deposits.

- Lipodissolve is not approved as a fat-reducing therapy by the FDA. Its safety and efficacy are not yet backed by scientific evidence.

Cloning for Medicine

Ian Wilmut

Ian Wilmut (1944–) grew up in Coventry, England, the son of a mathematics teacher and housewife. He earned an honors degree in agricultural science at the University of Nottingham and a Ph.D. from Cambridge University, specializing in methods of deep-freeze preservation of boar semen. Wilmut completed other scientific work, on deep-freeze techniques with animal embryos and on the causes of prenatal death in sheep and pigs, before turning to his highly publicized work in cloning. He and his team of scientists at the Roslin Institute near Edinburgh, Scotland announced the birth of Dolly—the first cloned mammal—in 1997 and generated a controversy that continues to spark heated ethical debate. In this article, he presents a "popularized" discussion of work that is discussed in highly technical fashion elsewhere. Note that as he presents the technical information in a readable way, he includes musings on the ethical questions that scientists are sometimes assumed to ignore.

1   In the summer of 1995 the birth of two lambs at my institution, the Roslin Institute near Edinburgh in Midlothian, Scotland, heralded what many scientists believe will be a period of revolutionary opportunities in biology and medicine. Megan and Morag, both carried to term by a surrogate mother, were not produced from the union of a sperm and an egg. Rather their genetic material came from cultured cells originally derived from a nine-day-old embryo. That made Megan and Morag genetic copies, or clones, of the embryo.

"Cloning for Medicine" by Ian Wilmut, published in *Scientific American*, December 1998.

Before the arrival of the lambs, researchers had already learned how to produce sheep, cattle and other animals by genetically copying cells painstakingly isolated from early-stage embryos. Our work promised to make cloning vastly more practical, because cultured cells are relatively easy to work with. Megan and Morag proved that even though such cells are partially specialized, or differentiated, they can be genetically reprogrammed to function like those in an early embryo. Most biologists had believed that this would be impossible.

We went on to clone animals from cultured cells taken from a 26-day-old fetus and from a mature ewe. The ewe's cells gave rise to Dolly, the first mammal to be cloned from an adult. Our announcement of Dolly's birth in February 1997 attracted enormous press interest, perhaps because Dolly drew attention to the theoretical possibility of cloning humans. This is an outcome I hope never comes to pass. But the ability to make clones from cultured cells derived from easily obtained tissue should bring numerous practical benefits in animal husbandry and medical science, as well as answer critical biological questions.

How to Clone

Cloning is based on nuclear transfer, the same technique scientists have used for some years to copy animals from embryonic cells. Nuclear transfer involves the use of two cells. The recipient cell is normally an unfertilized egg taken from an animal soon after ovulation. Such eggs are poised to begin developing once they are appropriately stimulated. The donor cell is the one to be copied. A researcher working under a high-power microscope holds the recipient egg cell by suction on the end of a fine pipette and uses an extremely fine micropipette to suck out the chromosomes, sausage-shaped bodies that incorporate the cell's DNA. (At this stage, chromosomes are not enclosed in a distinct nucleus.) Then, typically, the donor cell, complete with its nucleus, is fused with the recipient egg. Some fused cells start to develop like a normal embryo and produce offspring if implanted into the uterus of a surrogate mother.

5   In our experiments with cultured cells, we took special measures to make the donor and recipient cells compatible. In particular, we tried to coordinate the cycles of duplication of DNA and those of the production of messenger RNA, a molecule that is copied from DNA

and guides the manufacture of proteins. We chose to use donor cells whose DNA was not being duplicated at the time of the transfer. To arrange this, we worked with cells that we forced to become quiescent by reducing the concentration of nutrients in their culture medium. In addition, we delivered pulses of electric current to the egg after the transfer, to encourage the cells to fuse and to mimic the stimulation normally provided by a sperm.

After the birth of Megan and Morag demonstrated that we could produce viable offspring from embryo-derived cultures, we filed for patents and started experiments to see whether offspring could be produced from more completely differentiated cultured cells. Working in collaboration with PPL Therapeutics, also near Edinburgh, we tested fetal fibroblasts (common cells found in connective tissue) and cells taken from the udder of a ewe that was three and a half months pregnant. We selected a pregnant adult because mammary cells grow vigorously at this stage of pregnancy, indicating that they might do well in culture. Moreover, they have stable chromosomes, suggesting that they retain all their genetic information. The successful cloning of Dolly from the mammary-derived culture and of other lambs from the cultured fibroblasts showed that the Roslin protocol was robust and repeatable.

All the cloned offspring in our experiments looked, as expected, like the breed of sheep that donated the originating nucleus, rather than like their surrogate mothers or the egg donors. Genetic tests prove beyond doubt that Dolly is indeed a clone of an adult. It is most likely that she was derived from a fully differentiated mammary cell, although it is impossible to be certain because the culture also contained some less differentiated cells found in small numbers in the mammary gland. Other laboratories have since used an essentially similar technique to create healthy clones of cattle and mice from cultured cells, including ones from nonpregnant animals.

Although cloning by nuclear transfer is repeatable, it has limitations. Some cloned cattle and sheep are unusually large, but this effect has also been seen when embryos are simply cultured before gestation. Perhaps more important, nuclear transfer is not yet efficient. John B. Gurdon, now at the University of Cambridge, found in nuclear-transfer experiments with frogs almost 30 years ago that the number of embryos surviving to become tadpoles was smaller when donor cells were taken from animals at a more advanced developmental stage. Our first results with mammals showed a similar pattern. All the cloning studies described so far show a consistent pattern of deaths during embryonic and fetal development, with laboratories reporting only 1 to 2 percent of embryos surviving to become live offspring. Sadly, even some clones that survive through birth die shortly afterward.

Clones with a Difference

The cause of these losses remains unknown, but it may reflect the complexity of the genetic reprogramming needed if a healthy offspring is to be born. If even one gene inappropriately expresses or fails to express a crucial protein at a sensitive point, the result might be fatal. Yet reprogramming might involve regulating thousands of genes in a process that could involve some randomness. Technical improvements, such as the use of different donor cells, might reduce the toll.

10

The ability to produce offspring from cultured cells opens up relatively easy ways to make genetically modified, or transgenic, animals. Such animals are important for research and can produce medically valuable human proteins.

The standard technique for making transgenic animals is painfully slow and inefficient. It entails microinjecting a genetic construct—a DNA sequence incorporating a desired gene—into a large number of fertilized eggs. A few of them take up the introduced DNA so that the resulting offspring express it. These animals are then bred to pass on the construct [see "Transgenic Livestock as Drug Factories," by William H. Velander, Henryk Lubon and William N. Drohan; SCIENTIFIC AMERICAN, January 1997].

In contrast, a simple chemical treatment can persuade cultured cells to take up a DNA construct. If these cells are then used as donors for nuclear transfer, the resulting cloned offspring will all carry the construct. The Roslin Institute and PPL Therapeutics have already used this approach to produce transgenic animals more efficiently than is possible with microinjection.

We have incorporated into sheep the gene for human factor IX, a blood-clotting protein used to treat hemophilia B. In this experiment we transferred an antibiotic-resistance gene to the donor cells along with the factor IX gene, so that by adding a toxic dose of the antibiotic neomycin to the culture, we could kill cells that had failed to take up the added DNA. Yet despite this genetic disruption, the proportion of embryos that developed to term after nuclear transfer was in line with our previous results.

The first transgenic sheep produced this way, Polly, was born in the summer of 1997. Polly and other transgenic clones secrete the human protein in their milk. These observations suggest that once techniques for the retrieval of egg cells in different species have been perfected, cloning will make it possible to introduce precise genetic changes into any mammal and to create multiple individuals bearing the alteration.

15   Cultures of mammary gland cells might have a particular advantage as donor material. Until recently, the only practical way to assess whether a DNA construct would cause a protein to be secreted in milk was to transfer it into female mice, then test their milk. It should be possible, however, to test mammary cells in culture directly. That will speed up the process of finding good constructs and cells that have incorporated them so as to give efficient secretion of the protein.   15

Cloning offers many other possibilities. One is the generation of genetically modified animal organs that are suitable for transplantation into humans. At present, thousand of patients die every year before a replacement heart, liver or kidney becomes available. A normal pig organ would be rapidly destroyed by a "hyperacute" immune reaction if transplanted into a human. This reaction is triggered by proteins on the pig cells that have been modified by an enzyme called alpha-galactosyl transferase. It stands to reason, then, that an organ from a pig that has been genetically altered so that it lacks this enzyme might be well tolerated if doctors gave the recipient drugs to suppress other, less extreme immune reactions.

Another promising area is the rapid production of large animals carrying genetic defects that mimic human illnesses, such as cystic fibrosis. Although mice have provided some information, mice and humans have different genes for cystic fibrosis. Sheep are expected to be more valuable for research into this condition, because their lungs resemble those of humans. Moreover, because sheep live for years, scientists can evaluate their long-term responses to treatments.

Creating animals with genetic defects raises challenging ethical questions. But it seems clear that society does in the main support research on animals, provided that the illnesses being studied are serious ones and that efforts are made to avoid unnecessary suffering.

The power to make animals with a precisely engineered genetic constitution could also be employed more directly in cell-based therapies for important illnesses, including Parkinson's disease, diabetes and muscular dystrophy. None of these conditions currently has any fully effective treatment. In each, some pathological process damages specific cell populations, which are unable to repair or replace themselves. Several novel approaches are now being explored that would provide new cells—ones taken from the patient and cultured, donated by other humans or taken from animals.

20   To be useful, transferred cells must be incapable of transmitting   20
new disease and must match the patient's physiological need closely. Any immune response they produce must be manageable. Cloned animals with precise genetic modifications that minimize the human immune response might constitute a plentiful supply of suitable cells. Animals might even produce cells with special properties, although any modifications would risk a stronger immune reaction.

Cloning could also be a way to produce herds of cattle that lack the prion protein gene. This gene makes cattle susceptible to infection with prions, agents that cause bovine spongiform encephalitis (BSE), or mad cow disease. Because many medicines contain gelatin or other products derived from cattle, health officials are concerned that prions from infected animals could infect patients. Cloning could create herds that, lacking the prion protein gene, would be a source of ingredients for certifiable prion-free medicines.

The technique might in addition curtail the transmission of genetic disease. Many scientists are now working on therapies that would supplement or replace defective genes in cells, but even successfully treated patients will still pass on defective genes to their offspring. If a couple was willing to produce an embryo that could be treated by advanced forms of gene therapy, nuclei from modified embryonic cells could be transferred to eggs to create children who would be entirely free of a given disease.

Some of the most ambitious medical projects now being considered envision the production of universal human donor cells. Scientists know how to isolate from very early mouse embryos undifferentiated stem cells, which can contribute to all the different tissues of the adult. Equivalent cells can be obtained for some other species, and humans are probably no exception. Scientists are learning how to differentiate stem cells in culture, so it may be possible to manufacture cells to repair or replace tissue damaged by illness.

Making Human Stem Cells

Stem cells matched to an individual patient could be made by creating an embryo by nuclear transfer just for that purpose, using one of the patient's cells as the donor and a human egg as the recipient. The embryo would be allowed to develop only to the stage needed to separate and culture stem cells from it. At that point, an embryo has only a few hundred cells, and they have not started to differentiate. In particular, the nervous system has not begun to develop, so the embryo has no means of feeling pain or sensing the environment. Embryo-derived cells might be used to treat a variety of serious diseases caused by damage to cells, perhaps including AIDS as well as Parkinson's, muscular dystrophy and diabetes.

25   Scenarios that involve growing human embryos for their cells are   25 deeply disturbing to some people, because embryos have the potential to become people. The views of those who consider life sacred from conception should be respected, but I suggest a contrasting view. The embryo is a cluster of cells that does not become a sentient being until much later in development, so it is not yet a person. In the U.K., the Human Genetics Advisory Commission has initiated a major public consultation to assess attitudes toward this use of cloning.

Creating an embryo to treat a specific patient is likely to be an expensive proposition, so it might be more practical to establish permanent, stable human embryonic stem-cell lines from cloned embryos. Cells could then be differentiated as needed. Implanted cells derived this way would not be genetically perfect matches, but the immune reaction would probably be controllable. In the longer term, scientists might be able to develop methods for manufacturing genetically matched stem cells for a patient by "dedifferentiating" them directly, without having to utilize an embryo to do it.

Several commentators and scientists have suggested that it might in some cases be ethically acceptable to clone existing people. One scenario envisages generating a replacement for a dying relative. All such possibilities, however, raise the concern that the clone would be treated as less than a complete individual, because he or she would likely be subjected to limitations and expectations based on the family's knowledge of the genetic "twin." Those expectations might be false, because human personality is only partly determined by genes. The clone of an extrovert could have a quite different demeanor. Clones of athletes, movie stars, entrepreneurs or scientists might well choose different careers because of chance events in early life.

Some pontificators have also put forward the notion that couples in which one member is infertile might choose to make a copy of one or the other partner. But society ought to be concerned that a couple might not treat naturally a child who is a copy of just one of them. Because other methods are available for the treatment of all known types of infertility, conventional therapeutic avenues seem more appropriate. None of the suggested uses of cloning for making copies of existing people is ethically acceptable to my way of thinking, because they are not in the interests of the resulting child. It should go without saying that I strongly oppose allowing cloned human embryos to develop so that they can be tissue donors.

It nonetheless seems clear that cloning from cultured cells will offer important medical opportunities. Predictions about new technologies are often wrong: societal attitudes change; unexpected developments occur. Time will tell. But biomedical researchers probing the potential of cloning now have a full agenda.

Gary I. Rothstein/epa/Corbis

Crew of the space shuttle Atlantis, November 20, 2007.

Mandatory Childhood Vaccinations

On January 1, 2009, New Jersey became the first state to require flu shots for children who attend licensed day care and pre-school programs. New Jersey now requires immunization (vaccinations) for 13 vaccine-preventable communicable diseases, more than any other state. New Jersey is not alone, however, in requiring vaccinations—all 50 states currently have some kind of school immunization requirement. (All 50 states also permit exemptions under certain conditions.)

Childhood Vaccinations Save Lives

The states' rationale is clear: childhood vaccines introduced since the 1950s have all but wiped out many communicable diseases in the United States, including measles, mumps, whooping cough (pertussis), polio, and diphtheria. In the 1940s and '50s, before vaccines against these diseases were available, the five diseases combined caused an estimated 900,000 cases of disease and 7,700 deaths per year. By 2004 there were only 27 deaths from all five diseases combined—a 99.6% reduction. The

number of cases of measles dropped from more than 500,000 per year before the measles vaccine was available to only 62 cases per year in recent years.

Recently, however, public health officials have noticed an uptick in the number of cases of measles and whooping cough, two diseases that are highly sensitive to vaccination rates. In the first seven months of 2008 there were more cases of measles than at any time since 1996. Most of the measles victims in 2008 had not been vaccinated, even though they were eligible for the vaccine (children under 12 months of age are not yet eligible).

Parents Resist Mandatory Vaccination

The rise in measles and whooping cough coincides with more than a doubling of exemptions from school immunization programs granted for "philosophical or personal beliefs" between 1991 and 2004. Why are parents increasingly refusing to have their children vaccinated when the evidence is so overwhelming that vaccinations prevent communicable diseases? Their reasons tend to fall into two categories: 1) a belief that the vaccines (or something in them) may be contributing to what they view as an epidemic of childhood chronic diseases, including especially autism, and 2) a dislike of government intervention into personal decisions.

Compared to parents who vaccinate their children, parents who choose not to vaccinate their children tend to believe that the risk of their child getting the disease is low and that the disease itself is not very severe. The latter view is understandable, because most parents today have not lived through a major outbreak of any communicable disease. Today's parents were born after the scourge of polio, for example. Polio killed nearly 10% of its victims and crippled countless others for life before the polio vaccine became available in 1955.

Public health officials are watching these developments with concern. Not all people in a community can be vaccinated, and so the prevention of widespread outbreaks of vaccine-preventable diseases in communities depends in part on "herd immunity." The concept is that when most people in a community (or herd) have been vaccinated, the disease has a much harder time spreading from individual to individual. In other words, high vaccination rates benefit the community overall (especially young children), in addition to protecting the individual who has been vaccinated. Says Dr. Anne Schuchat, director of the National Center for Immunization and Respiratory Diseases, "The vaccine against measles is highly effective in preventing infections, and high immunization levels in the community are effective at preventing or drastically reducing the size of outbreaks."[1]

A Link Between Vaccinations and Autism?

Parents who oppose mandatory vaccinations for safety reasons often point to cases of children who developed autism shortly after receiving a vaccine. Their celebrity spokesperson is actress and former *Playboy* model Jenny McCarthy, whose son is autistic. Ms. McCarthy is on the board of Generation Rescue, a nonprofit organization that claims to be able to treat autism effectively with a special diet.

WENN/Newscom

Actress Jenny McCarthy has appeared on the Oprah Winfrey Show opposing mandatory vaccinations.

Medical professionals and research scientists continue to point out that the available scientific evidence does not support the argument that vaccination can cause childhood diseases, including autism. But for many parents, scientific studies are not as convincing as an appearance by Ms. McCarthy on the Oprah Winfrey Show with an emotional story about ill children.

Some parents oppose mandatory childhood vaccinations because they are philosophically opposed to government intervention into what they see as a personal choice. Says Barbara Loe Fisher, a mother and the cofounder of the National Vaccine Information Center, representing parents against forced vaccinations, "… If the State can tag, track down and force citizens against their will to be injected with biologicals of unknown toxicity today, there will be no limit on which individual freedoms the State can take away in the name of the greater good tomorrow."[2]

Parents in favor of vaccines are mounting lobbying campaigns as well. Their celebrity advocate is actress Amanda Peet, now a spokesperson for Every Child By Two, a vaccine-advocacy group founded by former first lady Rosalynn Carter. Ms. Peet once called anti-vaccine parents "parasites" for relying on other children's immunity to protect their own. She later apologized for the word, and suggested that parents should get their advice from doctors, not celebrities like herself (and presumably Ms. McCarthy).

It would be a shame if vaccines became such a hot-button issue that preventable diseases such as polio returned. We need to find a way to address parents' concerns about vaccine safety and about the role of government in our lives, while at the same time protecting the public from preventable, communicable diseases. How we choose to do that is up to all of us.

Questions to consider

1 What should medical professionals, politicians, or even just concerned citizens do, if anything, to help parents understand the risks and benefits of vaccines?

2 Will you vaccinate your children? Why or why not? What would you like to know in order to make an informed decision?

---

[1] www.cdc.gov/media/pressrel/2008/r080821.htm
[2] www.vaccineawakening.blogspot.com

The facts…

- **Childhood vaccination programs have been effective in all but eliminating certain communicable diseases.**

- **All 50 states have childhood vaccination (immunization) programs as a requirement for school attendance—all states also allow for certain exemptions.**

- **Exemptions from vaccination (and communicable diseases) are on the rise. Many parents object to mandatory vaccination programs out of concern that the vaccines may cause autism or certain other chronic childhood diseases.**

- **The available scientific evidence does not support the argument that vaccinations can cause childhood diseases, including autism.**

HIV Sufferers
Have a Responsibility

Amitai Etzioni

*Amitai Etzioni (1929–) was born in Cologne, Germany.
Educated at Hebrew University in Jerusalem (B.A., 1954)
and the University of California at Berkeley (M.A., 1956,
and Ph.D., 1958), Etzioni has directed the Center for Policy Research at Columbia University and taught at George
Washington University. Published widely, Etzioni has
written for both scholarly and lay audiences. He also has
edited a journal,* Responsive Community. *His books include* The Spirit of Community: Rights, Responsibilities, and the Communitarian Agenda *(1993). In this
essay, which appeared in* Newsweek *in 1993, Etzioni argues that HIV sufferers must disclose their illness for the
good of society, regardless of the personal consequences.*

1   A major drive to find a cure for AIDS was announced last week
by Donna Shalala, President Clinton's Secretary of Health and
Human Services. Researchers from the private sector, gay activists and government officials were teamed up to accelerate the
search for an effective treatment. Yet even highly optimistic observers
do not expect a cure to be found before the end of this century. Still,
as the Shalala announcement's exclusive focus on cure highlights, it is
not acceptable to explore publicly the measures that could curb the
spread of the disease by slowing the transmission of HIV, the virus that
causes it. Indeed, before you can say What about prevention? the politically correct choir chimes in: You cannot call it a plague! You are
feeding the fires of homophobia! Gay basher!

Case in point: a panel of seven experts fielded questions from
4,000 personnel managers at a conference in Las Vegas. "Suppose you

work for medical records. You find out that Joe Doe, who is driving the company's 18-wheeler, is back on the bottle. Will you violate confidentiality and inform his supervisor?" The panel stated unanimously, "I'll find a way." Next question: "Joe Smith is HIV positive; he is intimate with the top designer of the company but did not tell; will *you?*" "No way," the panel agreed in unison.

We need to break the silence. It is not antigay but fully compassionate to argue that a massive prevention drive is a viable way to save numerous lives in the very next years. We must lay a moral claim on those who are likely to be afflicted with HIV (gays, drug addicts who exchange needles and anyone who received a blood transfusion before 1985) and urge them as a social obligation to come forward to be tested. If the test is positive, they should inform their previous sexual contacts and warn all potential new ones. The principle is elementary, albeit openly put: the more responsibly HIV sufferers act, the fewer dead they will leave in their trail.

HIV testing and contact tracing amount to "a cruel hoax," claims a gay representative from the West Coast. "There are not enough beds to take care of known AIDS patients. Why identify more?" Actually, testing is cruel only in a world where captains of sinking ships do not warn passengers because the captains cannot get off. We must marshal the moral courage to tell those infected with HIV: It is truly tragic that currently we have no way to save your life, but surely you recognize your duty to try to help save the lives of others.

5 "Warning others is unnecessary because everybody should act safely all the time anyhow," argues Rob Teir, a gay activist in Washington. But human nature is such, strong data show, that most people cannot bring themselves to act safely all the time. A fair warning that they are about to enter a highly dangerous situation may spur people to take special precautions. The moral duty of those already afflicted, though, must be clearly articulated: being intimate without prior disclosure is like serving arsenic in a cake. And not informing previous contacts (or not helping public authorities trace them without disclosing your name) leaves the victims, unwittingly, to transmit the fatal disease to uncounted others.

Testing and contact tracing may lead to a person's being deprived of a job, health insurance, housing and privacy, many civil libertarians fear. These are valid and grave concerns. But we can find ways to protect civil rights without sacrificing public health. A major AIDS-prevention campaign ought to be accompanied by intensive public education about the ways the illness is not transmitted, by additional safeguards on data banks and by greater penalties for those who abuse HIV victims. It may be harsh to say, but the fact that an individual may suffer as a result of doing what is right does not make doing so less of an imperative. Note also that while society suffers a tremendous loss of talent and youth and is stuck with a gargantuan bill, the first victims of nondisclosure are the loved ones of those already afflicted with HIV, even—in the case of infected women—their children.

"Not cost effective," intone the bean counters. Let's count. Take, for example, a suggestion by the highly regarded Centers for Disease Control and Prevention that hospitals be required to ask patients whose blood is already being tested whether they would consent to having it tested for HIV as well. The test costs $60 or less and routinely identifies many who were unaware they had the virus. If those who are thus identified were to transmit the disease to only one less person on average, the suggested tests would pay for themselves much more readily than a coronary bypass, PSA tests and half the pills we pop. And society could continue to enjoy the lifelong earnings and social contributions of those whose lives would be saved.

There are other excuses and rationalizations. But it is time for some plain talk: if AIDS were any other disease—say, hepatitis B or tuberculosis—we would have no trouble (and indeed we have had none) introducing the necessary preventive measures. Moreover, we should make it clear that doing all you can to prevent the spread of AIDS or any other fatal disease is part and parcel of an unambiguous commandment: Thou shalt not kill.

The Immune System and Mechanisms of Defense

Colorized TEM (× 25,000) of a mast cell containing granules of histamine (dark purple).

AIDS: A Crisis in Africa, a Challenge for the World

Africa is in the midst of an AIDS epidemic. What is AIDS, how bad is the epidemic, how will it affect us, and what (if anything) are we willing to do about it?

In Africa, AIDS Is Out of Control

AIDS stands for *acquired immune deficiency syndrome*. It is caused by a virus that attacks the immune system, called *human immunodeficiency virus* (HIV). Approximately two-thirds of the world's HIV-infected people live in sub-Saharan Africa. The United Nations estimates that 22.4 million people there are already infected with HIV. The region accounts for more than three-quarters of the world's AIDS deaths.

Patterns of AIDS infection and transmission in Africa differ from those of industrialized countries. In the United States, more men than women are infected with HIV, which is often transmitted via homosexual sex. In Africa, however, an estimated 60% of HIV-infected persons are women who have contracted the virus heterosexually. Studies in several African nations have found that females aged 15–19 are four to five times more likely to be infected than males their age. According to one report, in Africa older HIV-infected men coerce or pay impoverished girls to have sex in the mistaken belief that sex with a virgin will cure AIDS.

The problem of AIDS in sub-Saharan Africa is made worse by political, economic, and social instability. Of the area's 42 nations, almost a third are at war. In many of these countries the economies are weak, sanitation is poor, and even rudimentary medical services are often lacking. Malnutrition and starvation are widespread. Approximately 11 million children in sub-Saharan Africa have been orphaned by AIDS, war, or famine. Many of them are abandoned and impoverished, fending for themselves without adult supervision.

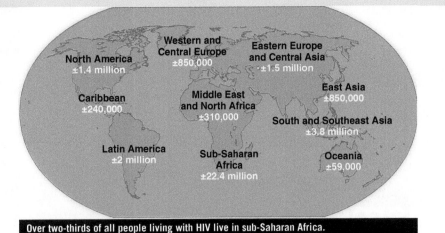

Region	Number
North America	±1.4 million
Western and Central Europe	±850,000
Eastern Europe and Central Asia	±1.5 million
Caribbean	±240,000
Middle East and North Africa	±310,000
East Asia	±850,000
South and Southeast Asia	±3.8 million
Latin America	±2 million
Sub-Saharan Africa	±22.4 million
Oceania	±59,000

Over two-thirds of all people living with HIV live in sub-Saharan Africa.

What can be done to help sub-Saharan Africa? Possibilities include:

- Providing accurate information on HIV transmission and helping people understand how their sexual practices may contribute to the spread of the disease.
- Seeking AIDS treatments and preventive measures that are inexpensive enough to be used effectively in poor countries.
- Providing economic assistance and encouraging political stability.
- Improving the delivery of health care.

These are all good ideas, of course. But any solution to the growing AIDS crisis in African countries must recognize that their problems are different from ours.

Roadblocks to Effective HIV Treatment

Strategies for treating HIV infection and preventing AIDS in sub-Saharan Africa face some significant obstacles not seen in North America. For example, improving the delivery of health care is difficult in rural areas without roads and bridges and in nations with too few medical personnel. Then there is the problem of identifying AIDS patients in the first place. As discussed in this chapter, people in North America who are suspected of having AIDS generally are tested for HIV. Most health professionals maintain careful records

documenting their patients' symptoms and treatments. In contrast, most African nations do not require that suspected AIDS patients be tested for HIV, and health professionals often can't monitor patients effectively or even pay for the tests to diagnose HIV infection. The diagnosis is made more difficult by the fact that other regional health problems, such as malnutrition, tuberculosis, and malaria, have symptoms that can resemble those of AIDS.

What about education? The type of public information campaigns used in North America may not be possible in countries with less developed media networks. Furthermore, social norms are different, and misinformation and denial are widespread. Sex education for both boys and girls and strategies to change men's sexual behavior are sorely needed. Providing male and female condoms at low cost might also help. In Thailand, a national program to promote condom use lowered the prevalence of HIV among 21-year-old military conscripts from 4% in the mid-1990s to less than 1% by 2002.

A final hurdle is the cost of treatment. Recent advances in AIDS treatment depend on new *antiretroviral* drugs (ARVs) that can cost up to $2,500 per month—more than many Africans earn in a year. High prices for new AIDS drugs reflect the enormous research and development costs that are

required by U.S. law to ensure drugs' safety and effectiveness. Foreign firms can manufacture and sell AIDS medicines at a fraction of the U.S. price because they do not have to recover the cost of drug development. In addition to selling the low-cost drugs abroad, foreign manufacturers sometimes smuggle them into North America. U.S. pharmaceutical firms claim that the knockoff ARVs endanger future research and the development of even better HIV treatments. They have struck back by taking legal action against distributors and purchasers of illegal AIDS medications.

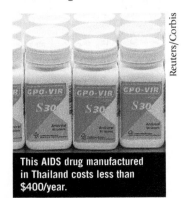

Reuters/Corbis

This AIDS drug manufactured in Thailand costs less than $400/year.

The global economic downturn of 2009 only made things worse. AIDS treatment programs suffered financially along with the rest of the economy. In addition, increased poverty usually leads to poorer nutrition, even less access to health care, and risky social behaviors such as trading sex for money.

The result of all of these problems is that in sub-Saharan Africa, fewer than half of all HIV-infected people currently receive treatment. Furthermore, only 60% of all patients who begin HIV treatment are still receiving it two years later. This is unfortunate, for ARVs should be taken for the rest of the patient's life in order to fully protect against the development of AIDS.

The challenge of AIDS in sub-Saharan Africa is likely to remain with us for some time. We can deal with it now or we can deal with an even larger problem later.

Questions to consider

1 Should foreign pharmaceutical companies be allowed to manufacture ARVs at low cost and sell them to needy nations?

2 As a matter of public health, should governments ensure that AIDS medicines are available to those who need them?

The facts...

- **Two-thirds of the world's HIV-infected people live in sub-Saharan Africa.**
- **In sub-Saharan Africa, girls aged 15–19 are four to five times more likely to be HIV-infected than boys.**
- **Attempts to solve the AIDS crisis in Africa are hampered by poor infrastructure, inadequate health care, poor medical record keeping, and educational, political, and social issues.**
- **Many African nations cannot afford the high cost of current AIDS treatment drugs.**

Al Gore's "Inconvenient Truth" Movie: Fact or Hype?

Stefan Lovgren

Stefan Lovgren, a writer for National Geographic, *has published articles on subjects as wide ranging as conservation in Cuba, manatees' migrating to the warm waters near power plants, and wormholes in space. In this selection from the* National Geographic News *web site, Lovgren investigates the claims made in former Vice President Al Gore's 2006 documentary,* An Inconvenient Truth. *Gore has long been an advocate for increasing awareness about climate change. His 1992 book,* Earth in the Balance: Ecology and the Human Spirit, *outlined the serious climatic and environmental issues facing the planet. The documentary, directed by Davis Guggenheim, won the 2006 Academy Award for a documentary feature; on the basis of his environmental work, Gore himself (along with the Intergovernmental Panel on Climate Change) won the Nobel Prize for Peace in 2007. Some critics charged that Gore's claims were either false, misleading, or erroneous; in order to test those claims, Lovgren consulted a number of noted scientists.*

1   The message in *An Inconvenient Truth,* the new movie starring former U.S. Vice President Al Gore, is clear: Humans are causing global warming, and the effects are devastating.

   Most scientists agree that the Earth is heating up, due primarily to an atmospheric increase in carbon dioxide caused mainly by the burning of fossil fuels such as coal and petroleum.

Reprinted from *National Geographic News*, May 25, 2006, by permission of The National Geographic Society.

But how accurate are some of the scientific claims made in the documentary?

In an attempt to clear the air, National Geographic News checked in with Eric Steig, an earth scientist at the University of Washington in Seattle, who saw *An Inconvenient Truth* at a preview screening.

5 He says the documentary handles the science well.

"I was looking for errors," he said.

"But nothing much struck me as overblown or wrong."

Claim: According to the film, the number of Category 4 and Category 5 hurricanes has almost doubled in the last year.

"This is true," Steig said. "There is no theoretical basis for the notion that this is a [natural] cycle."

10 A study published in the journal *Nature* in August ("Is Global Warming Making Hurricanes Worse?) found that hurricanes and typhoons have become more powerful over the past 30 years.

The study also found that these upswings in hurricane strength correlate with a rise in sea-surface temperatures. Ocean heat is the key ingredient for hurricane formation.

Experts emphasize that neither Hurricane Katrina nor any other single event can be linked to global warming.

"But," Steig said, "the statistics [show] that such events are more likely now than they used to be and will become more likely in the future."

Some scientists, however, believe that we are in the high-intensity stage of a decades-long natural hurricane cycle, which they say is primarily responsible for any uptick in storm activity.

15 Still others aren't even sure hurricanes are gaining strength.

"I've got real concerns about whether this is a real change or whether it's an artifact of the data," Christopher Landsea told National Geographic News in a story published in September ("Hurricanes Are Getting Stronger, Study Says"). Landsea is a researcher with the National Hurricane Center in Miami, Florida.

He noted that scientists now generally use satellite data to gauge hurricane stregth. This technique has greatly improved over the past 30 years, so earlier measurements may depict older hurricanes as weaker than they actually were, he said.

Claim: Heat waves will be more frequent and more intense as temperatures rise.

"There's no question about this," the University of Washington's Steig said. "If the average is going up, the extremes have to go up as well."

20   2005 was the hottest year on Earth since the late 19th century, when scientists began collecting temperature data. The past decade featured five of the warmest years ever recorded, with the second hottest year being 1998.

Claim: Deaths from global warming will double in just 25 years to 300,000 people a year.

"The exact numbers are, at best, an extrapolation from [a heat wave that] was experienced in Europe in 2003," Steig said.

"However, there is no question that that heat wave was a major event and statistically very unlikely to have happened unless the statistics are changing.

"Since it did happen, the statistics are changing—that is, the globe really is warming up."

25   **Claim: More than a million species worldwide could be driven to extinction in just half a century as a result of global warming.**

Steig is "skeptical that climate change itself will cause this [extinction] . . . so much as direct human impacts such as land-clearing." But he noted that he hadn't read the latest studies, some of which do make such a claim.

For example, a study published in *Nature* in 2004 ("By 2050 Warming to Doom Million Species, Study Says") predicted that climate change could drive more than a million species towards extinction by 2050.

"Climate change now represents at least as great a threat to the number of species surviving on Earth as habitat destruction and modification," said the lead author of that study, Chris Thomas, a conservation biologist at the University of Leeds in the United Kingdom.

Claim: Global warming will also cause the introduction of new, invasive species.

30   "I take issue with the invasive-species linkage, because the human influence—directly, by transporting species around—I suspect is much more important than climate change," Steig said.

Claim: Global sea levels could rise by more than 20 feet (6 meters) with the loss of shelf ice in Greenland and Antarctica, devastating coastal areas worldwide.

There is little doubt that sea levels would rise by that much if Greenland melted.

But scientists disagree on when it could happen.

A recent *Nature* study suggested that Greenland's ice sheet will begin to melt if the temperature there rises by 3°C (5.4°F) within the next hundred years, which is quite possible, according to leading temperature-change estimates.

35 "It's uncertain how much warmer Greenland would get, [given] a certain carbon dioxide level, because different climate models give different amounts of warming," said Jonathan Overpeck, director of the Institute for the Study of Planet Earth at the University of Arizona in Tucson.

But many experts agree that even a partial melting would cause a one-meter (three-foot) rise in sea levels, which would entirely submerge low-lying island countries, such as the Indian Ocean's Maldives.

Claim: The Arctic Ocean could be ice-free in summer by 2050.

Some climate models are more conservative, suggesting that there will be no summer ice in the Arctic by the year 2100.

But new research shows it could take as little as 20 years for the sea ice to disappear.

40 "Since the advent of remote satellite imaging, we've lost about 20 percent of sea-ice cover," said Mark Serreze, a research scientist at the National Snow and Ice Data Center in Boulder, Colorado.

"We're setting ourselves up for very big losses this year."

"We think of the Arctic as the heat sink to the climate system," Serreze said.

"We're fundamentally changing this heat sink, and we don't know how the rest of the climate system is going to respond."

There is no doubt that as sea ice continues to melt, habitat for animals like polar bears will continue to shrink.

Sensory Mechanisms

Colorized SEM of the surface of the tongue, showing papillae (pointing toward the back of the tongue).

DWD: Driving While Distracted

Linda Doyle died on September 3, 2008, when her Toyota Rav4 was struck broadside by a Ford pickup truck in an intersection in Oklahoma City. The 20-year-old driver of the truck, a college student named Christopher Hill, admitted to police that he ran a red light at 45 miles per hour because he had been distracted by a cell phone call. Asked what color the light was when he went through it, he said, "I never saw it."

Your brain receives sensory inputs from many different sources at once. It copes with all this sensory input by focusing on input considered most important at the moment, sometimes at the expense of other input. Anything that distracts you while driving is likely to lower your ability to drive safely. Distractions may be visual (taking your eyes off the road), cognitive (thinking about something else), or manual (taking your hands off the wheel). Typical distractions include texting or talking on the phone, putting on makeup, eating, reading, or using a navigation system. Some distractions, such as texting, are especially risky because they involve all three types of distractions at once (visual, cognitive, *and* manual).

According to the National Highway Traffic Safety Administration (NHTSA), more than half a million injuries and nearly 6,000 deaths a year are due to car crashes involving distracted drivers. The highest proportion of distracted drivers involved in fatal crashes are under 20 years old.

Driving while on the phone is the most common distraction. The NHTSA recommends that drivers not use their

Christopher Hill

cell phones while driving except in an emergency, but it doesn't appear that anyone is listening. According to the NHTSA, at any given moment during daylight hours nearly 800,000 drivers are on their cell phones while driving

Reacting to the statistics and to high-profile deaths like Linda Doyle's, some states are beginning to take action. Six states (California, Oregon, Washington, New Jersey, New York, and Connecticut) now prohibit all drivers from using handheld cell phones while driving. Nineteen states prohibit text messaging. Seventeen states and the District of Columbia have placed special restrictions on cell phone use by drivers with learner's permits or drivers under a certain age. Other states are likely to follow suit.

The use of handheld cell phones is not illegal yet in Oklahoma but Linda Doyle's daughter, Jennifer Smith, continues to press lawmakers for change. She's also suing Samsung, maker of the phone used by the driver, and the Sprint Nextel

service that provided the phone coverage in the area. The suit alleges that the companies failed to warn consumers about the dangers of driving while using their product. Sprint Nextel says that it includes adequate safety messages in its packaging, user manuals, advertising, and even on its Web site.

According to legal experts, Ms. Smith's lawsuit faces an uphill battle because crashes are caused by drivers, not cell phones, and because deep down inside, most drivers understand that talking on the phone while driving is a distraction but they continue to do it anyway. Lawyers for Samsung and Sprint Nextel are likely to argue that the companies had no responsibility to Linda Doyle because she did not use their phone or phone service; their only responsibility is to the young man who was driving the other vehicle, and he's not suing them.

Nevertheless, momentum is building to do something about the number of accidents being attributed to distracted drivers. "Every single time someone takes their eyes or their focus off the road—even for just a few seconds—they put their lives and the lives of others in danger," said Transportation Secretary Ray LaHood at a national summit on distracted driving. "Distracted driving is unsafe, irresponsible and in a split second, its consequences can be devastating."

Christopher Hill, the driver of the pickup truck that killed Linda Doyle,

and Jennifer Smith, her daughter, would undoubtedly agree. Christopher Hill plead guilty to negligent homicide (a misdemeanor) and was sentenced to five years of probation plus 240 hours of community service. He deeply regrets the accident and took responsibility for his actions, saying it was his choice to talk on the phone while driving. Linda Doyle's family says they have forgiven him. These days he talks to schools and community groups about the dangers of driving while distracted. Jennifer Smith, for her part, is now a spokesperson for FocusDriven, the first national nonprofit organization for increasing awareness about the dangers of driving while distracted.

Both Christopher Hill and Jennifer Smith say they no longer use their cell phones while driving.

Jennifer Smith

Questions to consider

1 Do you think that texting while driving should be illegal nationwide? What about talking on a handheld phone?

2 When you cross a state line, how do you know whether texting or using a phone is illegal in the state you are entering? Should you be told?

3 In several states (Utah and New Hampshire), using a handheld phone is a violation only if the driver commits another moving offense while on the phone. Is that a reasonable solution?

The facts...

- More than 6,000 deaths and 500,000 injuries per year are attributed to driving while distracted.
- At any given moment during daylight hours, more than 800,000 drivers are talking on their cell phones.
- The highest proportion of distracted drivers is under 20 years old.
- Laws against driving while distracted (texting, talking on a handheld phone) vary from state to state, from complete bans to no ban at all. There is no national standard.

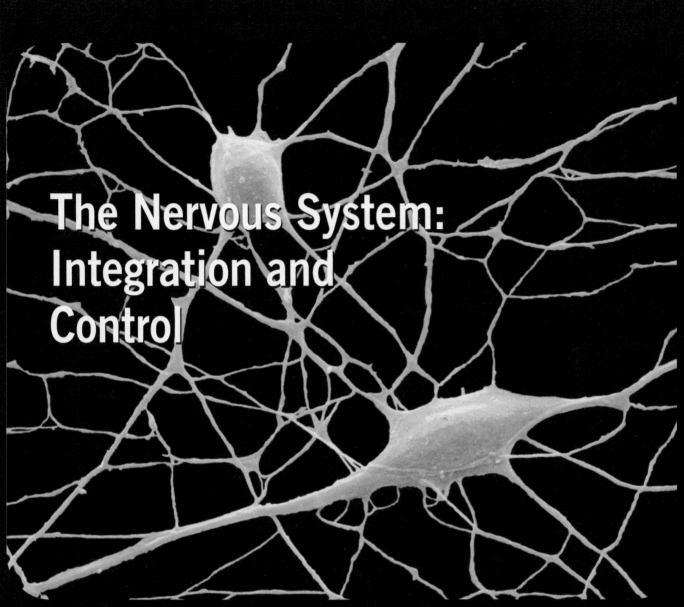

John Burbidge/Science Photo Library/Photo Researchers

Colored SEM (× 2,700) of two nerve cells from the cerebellum of the human brain.

Medically Induced Coma

Ariel Sharon, former prime minister of Israel, suffered a massive stroke and deteriorated rapidly. Randal McCloy, the sole survivor of a West Virginia mining accident, was close to death from carbon monoxide poisoning when he was rescued. Minutes after Mexican boxer Ruben Contreras stopped fighting in the sixth round of a scheduled eight-round bout, he had a seizure and collapsed. One month after being bitten by a bat, Wisconsin teenager Jeanna Giese almost died from rabies, a viral infection.

What do these people have in common? Although their circumstances were different, each suffered some type of injury to the brain. And in each case they were placed in a medically induced coma in a last-ditch effort to save their lives.

A Treatment of Last Resort for Brain Injuries

In a typical brain injury, fluid leaks out of capillaries in the injured area, causing swelling. Because the brain is enclosed in a rigid skull, the swelling leads to a rise in fluid pressure within

the skull that constricts the capillaries, cutting off blood flow and reducing oxygen delivery. Deprived of oxygen, healthy brain cells that could have survived the injury begin to die within minutes. In other words, in many cases it's the swelling that results from a brain injury that causes most of the damage, not the initial injury itself.

Treatment for brain injury generally centers on limiting the degree of swelling and subsequent oxygen deprivation. The patient is rushed to a hospital, where a breathing tube is inserted into the airway

Morry Cash/AP Wide World Photos

Jeanna Giese was placed in a coma after contracting rabies. She leaves the hospital as the first unvaccinated victim in the world to survive the disease.

so that a respirator can take over the breathing function. Physicians may inject a drug called *mannitol* to reduce brain swelling, or cool the patient's body to 90°F to lower the metabolic rate. Sometimes part of the skull is removed surgically to give brain tissue room to swell.

Medically induced coma is a treatment of last resort. Physicians administer a large dose of a barbiturate or sedative drug, which induces the coma. An electroencephalogram (EEG) recording of brain electrical activity shows flat waves with no brain activity at all, and the person literally appears to be dead. EEG monitoring continues, and drug levels are adjusted accordingly to ensure that the brain stays "asleep."

Why is a medically induced coma thought to be a good idea in some extreme cases? Over half of the brain's metabolic activity (and hence requirement for oxygen) is related to the electrical activity of brain cells; the remainder is for basic cell functions required by all cells. In theory, drastically reducing brain neural activity by

inducing a coma should reduce the brain's consumption of oxygen and glucose by half. A lower metabolic rate should lower blood flow and blood pressure within the capillaries of the brain and that, in turn, should reduce brain swelling. Medically induced coma is thought to buy time for the brain to heal.

But Does It Work?

Medicating an already critically ill individual into a coma is likely to be risky. An immobilized patient may develop atelectasis (collapsed alveoli or fluid-filled alveoli in the lungs) and pneumonia, for it's not possible to ask a comatose patient to get up and walk or even to take a deep breath or cough to avoid developing these conditions. A complete lack of activity may lead to blood clots that can be fatal if they migrate to the lungs. Some patients develop persistent muscle weakness or paralysis that can linger for weeks even after they come out of the coma. Furthermore, it is impossible for physicians to assess the extent of brain damage until the person is aroused.

Although there are several good scientific studies showing that medically induced coma does reduce swelling and fluid pressure in the brain in patients after head trauma, it is not clear that medically induced coma actually improves patient outcomes or quality of life. One retrospective study reported the outcomes of 38 patients who had been placed in medically induced comas after head injuries. Over half of the patients died during intensive care for their head injuries and four others were left severely disabled or remained in a chronic vegetative state. Only six patients had returned to work. Although these data might suggest that medically induced coma is of little or no benefit, the results are not conclusive because they do not separate

the negative effects of the head injuries from the effects (positive or negative) of the medically induced coma. A carefully controlled prospective study of a group of brain injury patients, half of whom were placed in a medically induced coma and half of whom were not, would have to be undertaken to answer this question. So far, the study has not been done.

And yet, there are success stories occasionally in the headlines. The physicians who placed Jeanna Giese in a coma for eight days are glad they took the risk. Today Ms. Giese is the only unvaccinated person ever to have survived rabies once the symptoms of the disease had developed. Randal McCloy survived his mining accident, came out of a medically induced coma, and has returned home. And Ruben Contreras was well enough to attend a boxing match less than four months after his seizure and subsequent coma. These are anecdotes, of course, but they're intriguing enough to cause physicians and medical researchers to wonder—does medically induced coma really work?

Mark J. Terrill/AP Wide World Photos

Boxer Ruben Contreras throws a punch in a match against Brian Viloria. Contreras suffered a seizure after the match and was placed in a coma during his treatment.

Questions to consider

1 If someone you love were to suffer a severe head injury, would you want that person placed in a medically induced coma? Would you want to be placed in one yourself? Why or why not?

2 What would you ask the physician in order to help you make an informed decision?

The facts...

- Medically induced coma is used to reduce brain metabolism and brain swelling in certain patients in an effort to limit or prevent brain damage.
- Physicians induce the coma by administering drugs that essentially put the brain to sleep.
- Medically induced coma remains a risky, last-ditch choice: while it can buy time for the brain to recover, it may lead to unrelated medical complications.

Conclusion
New Frontiers: Science and
Choice in the New Millennium

———————

In 1995, the Natural Law Party ran candidate John Hagelin, a Transcendental Meditation disciple with a doctorate in physics from Harvard University, in the American presidential election. During the campaign, the party offered a scientific demonstration of the power of Transcendental Meditation to bring peace to a troubled world. More than 5,000 disciples gathered in Washington, DC to meditate, with the purpose of bringing peace to a notoriously violent city. A year later, the party released a study that "scientifically" proved that Washington had indeed been more peaceful because of the waves of love and harmony projected by the meditators. When it was pointed out that the crime rate in the city during the demonstration was actually much higher than normal, the party defended its study on the basis that, without the meditators, the crime rate would have been even higher.

The case of the yogic peace waves highlights the power and problem of science at the beginning of the twenty-first century. Because we have come to accept and even expect wondrous things to come from science, it has become easier to make wild or even fraudulent claims of discovery so long as the claim is draped in scientific terms or supported by someone who claims to have scientific credentials. If a person with a PhD in physics says something is scientifically proven, shouldn't the general public accept the reality of the claim? After all, what higher standard of scientific expertise is there than a doctoral degree in physics?

Our understanding of what science is and how it interacts with our society has been fundamentally altered. For the Greeks, the study of nature was an elite, highly controlled activity, undertaken by a tiny intellectual cadre with philosophical and religious objectives. For people living in the twenty-first century, science is an incredibly powerful tool for political, economic, and social change. Everyone now claims some knowledge of science, and many, such as the Natural Law Party, claim the mantle of science as a way of demonstrating the importance, objectivity, and ultimate truth of their ideas. At the same time, scientific investigations of nature, still performed by elite, highly trained experts, continue to make great forays into new understandings and manipulations of nature.

How did this change take place? Gradually, state leaders—princes and governments—began to see the utility of science and scientists, either to elevate their status as cultural and intellectual leaders or to boost their military and economic power and well-being. Sixteenth-century natural philosophers, providing status and spectacle for European princely courts, are the linear ancestors of the Manhattan Project and Big Science funded by the government and military. Scientists themselves contributed to this transformation, arguing for the usefulness of their investigations even when this was not the case. Here the parallels between the rhetoric of early Royal Society statements and that of modern grant applications is instructive. Granting agencies want to know what they will get out of the relationship in exchange for the money and connections they offer. As the power of scientists has increased, so has the value of association with science.

The result of this transformation of science is paradoxical. On the one hand, twenty-first-century science has the power to transform our lives and our understanding of the universe in ways we can barely imagine. The huge resources now available to scientists, the tools at their disposal, and society's belief in the beneficence of science in general all contribute to the potential flowering of fascinating and significant scientific results. On the other hand, this widespread exposure to science has led to both a fear of the power of science and a credulity that allows scientific charlatans to flog their wares with impunity. There is reason in both these positions. Science has shown its terrifyingly brutal face in the twentieth century, and for many interested in peace or the environment, the way of science does not seem to offer any answers to the massive problems facing us. Equally, science has become so complex that laypeople cannot understand it, and so those claiming scientific discoveries and breakthroughs receive favourable reporting in the press and widespread acceptance with little critical examination.

The power of science, the legitimate fear of its misuse, and a gullible misunderstanding of scientific principles are all the result of the triumph of science since the scientific revolution. The challenge now will be to expand our understanding of the idea of science and to use our informed judgment to improve the world and keep it safe.

WHAT IS SCIENCE? PROFESSIONALIZATION AND SELF-REGULATION

One of the ways we can see the transformation of science in our society is in the act of talking about science, which has become more complicated. The term "science" has been remade. While it has never had a universally accepted definition, it once was commonly regarded as referring only to the study of the physical world and the tools and methods of that study. The term has now become a general indicator of a claim for any profound or specialized knowledge. Adding "science" to a phrase is often an attempt to make whatever it is attached to seem more certain, insightful, true, or useful. The phrases "science of hair care," "the science of business management," "political science," or "created by a leading scientist" attempt to tie a product to the idea of science, even if under minimal scrutiny there is no practical or historical link to science (in its traditional form) whatsoever.

Even before the members of the Royal Society and the Académie des Sciences began to promote the concept of the utility of science as a justification for the existence of their organizations, the utility of science had been integral to the ethos of research. Patrons were looking for more than philosophical insight when they employed natural philosophers, and, like Archduke Cosimo, we have come to expect science to provide more than esoteric knowledge. The successful exploitation of science has been demonstrated so powerfully over the last 400 years that nations now neglect it at their peril. It has changed the course of wars, helped raise up countries economically, and changed gender relations. Science is now so closely linked to the success of nations that it is a mandatory subject of education in all industrialized nations and many others. Every child must learn science to gain productive employment and good citizenship. The degree of integration of science education is one indicator of what separates the developed from the developing world.

Science has been so broadly injected into industrial society that it is difficult to distinguish what science is and even who is a "scientist." While we readily acknowledge the science Nobel Prize winners as scientists, does the category include people with advanced degrees who do no original research, such as purity control chemists? Physicians receive a great deal of scientific training, so are general practitioners scientists or does the term apply only to medical researchers? Psychoanalysts, homeopaths, computer programmers, and sociologists have at one time or another claimed scientist status. A hominid paleobiologist and a cultural anthropologist may work in the same department at a university, but are they both scientists? Clearly, there is a spectrum of careers from very scientific to no science required, but the range and number of people claiming science status has expanded enormously.

The functionalist definition that "Science is what scientists do" has started to break down in the modern world and will break down even more in the future as the trend to claim scientific status by a wider and wider range of people continues. This will make the problem of informed choices about scientific issues even harder. In the era of the greatest number of working scientists and the widest teaching of science in human history, the very concept of scientific knowledge can become muddled. The number of people claiming to offer scientific insight has become legion, so there is frequently conflicting "expert" opinion on a variety of socially important issues. Whether it is in a murder trial or a debate about global warming, scientific experts with equivalent credentials may offer diametrically opposed opinions. As science has had a greater direct effect on society and more people can claim to be doing science, v have seen a rise in the misunderstanding, or misrepresentation, of scientific ideas. Further, outright fraud cloaked as science has become easier.

With the expectation that science can make astonishing discoveries and produce wondrous devices, it did not seem completely unrealistic in 1989 that a new energy source had been discovered. When Chase Peterson, president of the University of Utah, announced that two scientists, Stanley Pons and Martin Fleischmann, had discovered fusion at room temperature, it caused a sensation. Their discovery was called "cold fusion" as opposed to the "hot fusion" seen in stars or hydrogen bombs. If the scientists had generated even a tiny bit more energy in their power cells than they had put in, their accomplishment could revolutionize energy production and, in the process, make large sums of money. Part of the excitement came from other scientists, especially physicists, who said that cold fusion could not possibly work, which provided good sound bites and an easy conflict to cover in the media.

In the days immediately after the announcement, it was not clear what Pons and Fleischmann had actually done, and so the idea that some new aspect of physics had been uncovered seemed possible. Some hastily constructed experiments at other labs appeared to confirm, or at least not clearly disprove, the claim. If cold fusion was real, physics would have to be revised, but such events had happened in the past. The unexpected results of a simple experiment heating up a black cube had, for example, helped initiate quantum physics.

Claims for cold fusion turned out to be completely unfounded, and there was no challenge to our understanding of physics, but the event highlights some of the problems of informed choice about science. The major characters in the story, Pons and Fleischmann, were reputable scientists with degrees, memberships in professional associations, and employment at major universities. They had all the credentials to make them reliable sources for scientific discovery, so it was not unreasonable to presume that their work merited serious consideration. That other scientists objected to their conclusions did not, in itself, make the work wrong. History is littered with stories of established scientists opposing new discoveries, from Priestley's objection to Lavoisier's oxygen theory, to the classical physicists' rejection of Einstein's theory of relativity, and the geological community's condemnation of Wegener's idea that continents move. The problem is that for every dismissed idea that triumphs, there are dozens of crazy ideas that turn out to be complete hogwash and deserve to be struck down. While most of these scientific struggles take place within the scientific community, Pons and Fleischmann played out their story in the full glare of media attention and with the backing of tremendous amounts of research money. The stakes are considerably higher in the era of Big Science: not only money, but people's time and effort, equipment and space, must be allocated for research. Although funding is not quite a zero-sum game in which the total amount of money available is fixed, it is close to that. While it is not clear how much money and time has been spent on the chimera of cold fusion, it is in the millions of dollars and thousands of laboratory hours that could have supported some other research effort.

There is a dictum in both science and law that extraordinary claims require extraordinary evidence. In the case of cold fusion, the claims were indeed extraordinary while the evidence was not available. Most commentators have attributed the "discovery" to wishful thinking and poor experimental procedures rather than malfeasance. Science does have a method of self-regulation, designed to squeeze unsound science out of the range of topics considered by scientists as legitimate or worthwhile. Scientists point to the peer review system in journals (not used by Pons and Fleischmann, who turned instead to the mass media) and to the replication of experiments as the internal means of weeding out bad science. This is, however, more problematic than you might think, since it turns out to be difficult to repeat some big experiments and few experiments are ever repeated in practice. Since scientists' livelihood is based on discovery, there is not much support for repeating work that has already been done. As well, since the cost of large-scale experiments, such as supercollider tests, can run into the millions of dollars, it may not be possible economically to repeat certain experiments even if there were some interest in doing so. Scientists, therefore, often rely on the consilience of experimental results, rather than on repeated experiments. In other words, experimental results are accepted as valid, even if not independently tested, if the results fall within expected norms, corresponding to already established theories, and if the experiment has been conducted following accepted procedures.

A second, and growing problem for self-regulation is the use of secrecy in research. While aspects of research of military importance have long been kept secret, more non-military research is being kept confidential, based on the idea of proprietary information not only in corporate-funded research, but also increasingly in public research, as universities and governments look to spin research off into profit-making businesses. If there is no evidence to evaluate, claims are hard to test, and timely decisions about research or products becomes difficult. Secrecy can affect both the discoveries, which are often shielded from public scrutiny, and the application of research, also kept secret. Legal settlements over product liability that have used scientific research often have included non-disclosure agreements or "gag orders" to prevent parties from revealing to others what problems were discovered. Such restrictions have been applied to a range of products from cigarettes to war chemicals. If scientific work cannot be examined by other scientists, then the self-regulation system breaks down.

Added to this problem are efforts by interested parties to protect their investments by interfering with scientific inquiry. This can take the form of biased research or efforts to block research that might indicate problems with a product or procedure. The most publicized cases have been in the pharmaceutical business in which a number of researchers have been fired, threatened with legal action, sued, or had funding withdrawn for publishing negative results or suggesting problems with drugs. Such was the case for Dr. Nancy Olivieri, who was threatened with legal action and removed from her position at Toronto's Sick Children's Hospital after publishing a negative report on the drug deferiprone in the *New England Journal of Medicine* in 1998. Although she was later reinstated, her case was far from isolated. The problem of biased research has become so urgent that in 2001 the International Committee of Medical Journal Editors issued a warning that they would no longer publish drug trial reports from researchers who were bound by agreements that limited academic freedom. In other words, it was the whole story or no story. Since new drugs can cost millions of dollars to produce and can generate billions of dollars in revenues, the pressure to publish positive research is very great. An increasing number of scientific journals now require a disclosure of financial interest, such as funding sources or corporate remuneration, from scientists submitting papers.

While interested parties may try to circumvent the publication of negative results, science journals are not always neutral players, so the self-regulatory mechanism of peer review is not completely reliable either. In recent years, even the most prestigious journals such as *Science* and *Nature* have been accused of rushing results into print in order to be the first to publish cutting-edge work. Because of the importance of publication, a kind of feedback loop exists between the scientists and the journals. Journals gain prestige by publishing exciting and ground-breaking results. Scientists who want to make a name for themselves aim to have their work published in prestige journals. This convergence of interests is not necessarily a problem, although it can encourage both players to take shortcuts. As well, the reliance on "blind" or anonymous reviewing for publication is not always impartial. In fields where everyone's work is known to everyone else, the control mechanism of peer review may break down. Since only scientists in the same field can understand and evaluate work, when they act as reviewers they may be reluctant to criticize other members of the same small community. The editors of scientific journals have little defence against bad work if the peer reviews on which they rely are biased or incomplete. The stakes are high. Millions of dollars in research money, leading research posts, international prestige, and the ultimate prize—a Nobel Prize—may ride on the status of publications.

The various problems of verification are a natural by-product of a complex and self-regulating profession, but it can make the interaction between scientists and the general public difficult. Lay people are left troubled by conflicting and often contradictory scientific claims, so it is no wonder that some have rejected the whole enterprise of science, greeting all new discoveries with skepticism. Ignoring science is putting one's head in the sand as it continues to change our lives, whether we like it or not. In the coming years, we as individuals and as a society will be faced with an increasing number of choices presented to us by science. Where should research money go? How will we assess the differential importance of demands for cash for a giant synchrotron to look into the interior of subatomic particles against space stations or the search for the cure for cancer? How do we balance the dangers against the potential benefits of creating genetically modified food in a world where starvation and pestilence are common? What about deeply personal choices, such as the potential to genetically modify our children or even ourselves?

Research that has occurred in the past few years has not been around long enough to come under historical scrutiny, but we can project some historical lines of work into the near future and look at a few examples of the intriguing and potentially world-changing ideas that are currently being investigated.

NANOTECHNOLOGY

One of the most intriguing, and in some ways subtle, areas of scientific research has been in materials science. In this area of work, which spans chemistry, physics, metallurgy, and, increasingly, biology, a host of new materials have been discovered or created. At the centre is carbon, particularly carbon fibres, which have already given us graphite tennis racquets and stealth aircraft. The next generation of nanotubes and buckminsterfullerenes, better known as bucky balls, may be even more revolutionary.

In 1985, Harold Kroto at the University of Sussex was wondering about carbon chains in space. Evidence suggested that certain stars, red dwarfs, produce a kind of soot. If this were the case, these carbon chains would be one of the oldest possible molecules, perhaps forming the foundation for a number of celestial objects and providing the materials to make up organic matter in the universe. To test this hypothesis, Kroto asked Richard Smalley and his team at Rice University in Houston to recreate some of the conditions that exist at the surface of a red dwarf star. Smalley had a device he called the laser-supersonic cluster beam apparatus. It consisted of a very high-powered laser (hot enough to duplicate star temperatures) and a high-speed stream of helium attached to a detector system to analyze the products. By shooting the laser at a block of carbon and collecting the vapourized clusters of molecules, they discovered that some of the molecules contained a fixed number of carbon atoms, either 60 or 70.

What had begun as a simple experiment of little interest outside a point of cosmology turned into a serious puzzle. Based on the geodesic dome design pioneered by R. Buckminister Fuller, Smalley, working much like

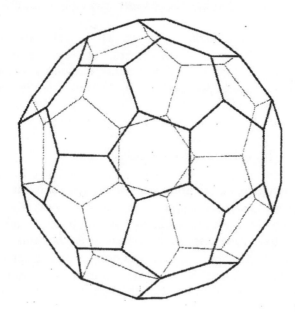

Watson and Crick, used paper cut-outs of hexagons and pentagons to construct a shape that had the required number of atoms and no unattached bonds left over. Thus the C_{60} bucky ball was discovered, and a new branch of carbon studies opened up. These molecules are very hardy; they don't interact much with other chemicals; they are incredibly resistant to being broken apart; and they can encapsulate another atom, locking it inside a carbon cage. The potential for batteries, lubricants, and catalytic materials based on the fullerenes seems very high.

Fullerenes can also be formed into tubes, called nanotubes, since they are about a nanometre in diameter.[1] These tubes, which theoretically can be of any length, suggested another kind of carbon product—super strong cables. Perhaps the most audacious use suggested for such carbon fibres was to create a 99,820 kilometre-long thread rising up from the equator to outer space. On the thread, or more accurately massive cable, shuttle cars would move up and down taking things to and from orbit. The idea of such a captive satellite was first visualized by Konstantin Tsiolkovsky (of Russian rocketry fame) in 1895 when he looked at the Eiffel Tower and imagined a cable rising up from it into space. One of the first examinations of the scientific possibility of a space elevator came from the team of John D. Isaacs, Allyn C. Vine (1914–94), Hugh Bradner (1915–), and George E. Bachus, who published "Satellite Elongation into a True 'Sky-Hook'," in the journal *Science* in 1966. Arthur C. Clarke used the idea in his novel *Fountains of Paradise* (1979) and said in a speech that same year that the space elevator "...will be built about fifty years after everyone stops laughing."[2] While the projected timeline for a space elevator is still uncertain, NASA's Institute for Advanced Concepts has given a $570,000 grant to Brad Edwards to study the project.

In addition to moving materials cheaply, the space elevator would also serve as a launch platform, flinging things into space at a velocity of more than 25,000 kilometres per hour, like a giant slingshot using the rotation of the earth. Building such a cable depends on creating a carbon thread strong enough to do the job, but, even if this turns out to be impossible or too costly for anyone in the near future, the development of lesser nanotubes may revolutionize building technology, replacing many of the steel components that surround us, from car bodies to airplane wings.

Although the first stage of manufacturing carbon composite materials has followed established large-plant petrochemical engineering, the next may feature the use of nanotechnology, which proposes to control directly, at the atomic level, the assembly of materials. It will use a system that creates materials by assembling them atom by atom into the desired molecules, thereby making it possible to create any material that does not contravene the laws of chemical bonding. A start towards this submicroscopic factory was made in 1981 when Gerd Binning (1947–) and Heinrich Rohrer (1933–), working at the IBM Research Lab in Zurich, created the first scanning tunnelling microscope (STM). Although it is called a microscope, it examines materials well below the range of any optical system. Rather than looking at small objects, it feels them in a way analogous to a phonograph needle feeling the contours in the groove of a vinyl record. With a current running through a very sharp needle, the STM can trace the outline of objects down to a hundredth of a nanometre. High-powered computers turn the data into a visual image.

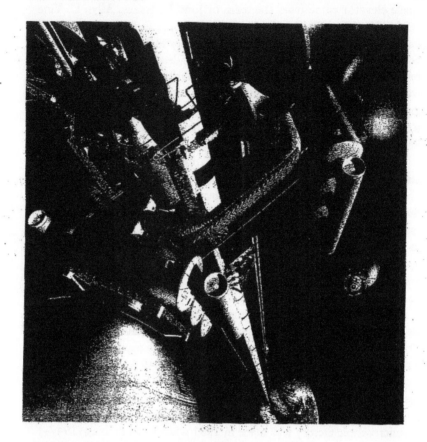

The microscope has a second trick up its sleeve, however. In addition to sensing small objects, it can pick them up and move them around. In 1989, another IBM team at Almaden, California, used an STM to arrange 35 xenon atoms to spell "IBM." This feat was topped in 1996 back in Zurich when a miniature abacus was constructed out of molecules with a diameter of less than one-millionth of a millimetre (in the manometre range). The abacus consisted of 11 rows of ten C_{60} fullerene molecules, which the tip of the STM pushed backwards and forwards to count. While an abacus that requires an STM to count may seem like a bit of a science stunt, it actually has a serious purpose. If nanotechnology is to be created, there has to be some way to make the original nanomachines. In a sense, the STM offers the possibility of creating the machine shop that will produce the machine-making machines.

Other researchers have developed microscopic pumps and motors, so the production of such micromachines seems entirely possible. Some scientists foresee nanofactories creating useful materials from piles of raw chemicals, from the molecular-level assembly of carbon-fibre materials to whole objects—chairs, computers, and airplanes—out of vats of basic elements. As futuristic as this may seem, the truth is that nanofactories already exist. They are called cells, where DNA and other component parts assemble atoms and molecules into a huge variety of materials such as electrical circuits (nerves), self-repairing fabric (skin), and structural supports (bone and chitin). Since the introduction of recombinant DNA techniques in 1972 and genome mapping in 1985, the biological sciences have given us unprecedented control over cell activity. Three aspects of these discoveries in genetics are already hitting the marketplace: testing, medical therapy, and genetically modified organisms.

GENETIC TESTING AND GENETIC THERAPIES

Genetic testing is, in some ways, a continuation of other forms of testing for diseases. Whether it is culturing blood to discover the presence of a disease organism or looking at tissue samples for signs of cancer, the first stage of genetic testing was based on looking for an indicator of some problem. For example, in 1983 James Gusella and his team identified Huntington's disease as a genetic anomaly on chromosome 4. As mapping has improved, the number of problem sites that can be identified has increased dramatically. Hundreds of tests now exist for diseases like cystic fibrosis, Tay-Sachs, Down's syndrome, and many others. Testing is also starting to reveal not only existing conditions, but also the potential for disease. This means that a person might, for example, have an elevated risk of getting a particular kind of cancer, although it is not a certainty.

While genetic testing offers a powerful weapon against disease, there are ethical issues about its use. One concerns ownership of tests. Since genes can be patented, tests based on certain gene lines have become private property. Patent holders have forced laboratories, both medical testing labs and research labs, to pay fees for certain tests or stop doing them, not because equipment or even techniques are being used without compensation, but because of ownership of specific genetic material. Who owns the genetic material of the globe, whether gathered or manufactured, is being hotly debated, especially in cases where the genetic material has been gathered from indigenous people, who may or may not have been informed of its potential use.

Another major issue has to do with the choices that stem from the information a genetic test provides. Genetic testing can reveal that people are carriers of problems that are not manifested in them, but might affect their children. Similarly, prenatal genetic tests can reveal some seriously debilitating diseases. In such cases, decisions about having children must be made, but such choices are difficult. For example, how bad does a problem have to be to warrant forgoing parenthood or terminating a pregnancy? Some argue that only the most severe handicaps should be tested for, since only the most severe cases justify intervention. Others argue that broad testing not only for clearly defined problems but also for elevated risks should be done, in order to give parents the greatest amount of information to assist in making an informed choice. Still others argue for no testing at all, since it may lead to making decisions about who lives or dies based on convenience, rather than on concepts of humanitarianism or the sanctity of life. Add to this the problem of accuracy, since a certain percentage of tests will be wrong, and the complexity of choice becomes even greater.

Genetic testing of a wide population has also been made possible, raising issues of privacy *versus* social benefit and of who has the right to information. Health care providers might be able to plan more rationally for services if they had genetic information about the general population, but such broad testing might also be used to deny insurance to people likely to develop costly health problems. Should employers be allowed to test employees to see if they are likely to get sick? Equally, a number of researchers have claimed that there are genetic links to behaviour, so that genetic testing might be used to identify people who are more susceptible to addiction or criminal behaviour. While it may sound like a bad science fiction story, we have the technology to create mass genetic databases on whole national populations, as was done in Iceland (see pages 399-400), and which is limited only by computer storage capacities.

While testing can indicate where problems lie, it is the ability to use genetics to repair problems that now attracts most interest. The first use of recombinant DNA in therapy was undertaken by a team working for the US National Institutes of Health (NIH). In 1990 and 1991 they used retroviruses to modify T-cells (part of the immune system) taken from two girls with a rare genetic disorder called adenosine deaminase deficiency. When the T-cells were returned to the patients, a certain portion of the T-cells being produced by the patients continued to be free of the genetic problem. Their health improved to the point where they were able to reduce their drug intake to half the amount used in conventional treatment of the disease. While this was not a complete cure, it was a remarkable change for the patients.

By 1995 more than 100 protocols for gene therapy had been reviewed and approved by the NIH. By 2003, the number has reached more than 1,000 treatments worldwide, although efficacy of some of the treatments is much in doubt. Many of the ethical concerns about genetic therapy have to do with limits to its use. While treating some genetically based diseases seems unproblematic, at what point is a therapy no longer about defence against disease, but about changing a person in order to reach some desired condition? Should gene therapy be developed for baldness or to make people taller?

The case of height is an interesting one, since it bridges both the pre-genetic and genetic treatment eras. The hormone HGH or Human Growth Hormone was isolated by Choh Hao Li (1913-87) and his team in 1956. While HGH is not the only control mechanism that affects human height, it was developed as a treatment for dwarfism in children in the 1960s. Over time, doctors started getting requests for HGH treatment for children who did not suffer from dwarfism, but were just shorter than average height or even at average height. This raised ethical questions about the use of therapy to improve the human body rather than ameliorate a debilitating condition.

The uncertainty associated with genetic therapy, and problems like the non-clinical use of HGH, led the NIH to establish a panel to examine the issue. As the history of HGH shows, the ethical questions are not theoretical. Although the panel's 1995 report argued that genetic therapy had many potential benefits, and future work looked very promising, it also warned people about too much enthusiasm:

> Overselling of the results of laboratory and clinical studies by investigators and their sponsors—be they academic, federal, or industrial—has led to the mistaken and widespread perception that gene therapy is further developed and more successful than it actually is. Such inaccurate portrayals threaten confidence in the integrity of the field and may ultimately hinder progress toward successful application of gene therapy to human disease.[3]

In 1985, the US Food and Drug Administration approved the marketing of HGH produced by genetically modified bacteria, the second genetically engineered drug after insulin to be introduced. While geneticists and physicians worked on these products with therapy in mind, promoters of the use of HGH touted it as a wonder drug that would increase muscle mass, decrease body fat, make a person look and feel younger, and even increase libido. While these claims are largely untrue, or at best unsubstantiated, promoters have used the scientific foundation of HGH work to justify wild claims and to send e-mail spam advertising their product to millions of people. Marketing and a fear of failing to keep up genetically with the next-door neighbours may drive the demand for therapy and provide ample opportunities for charlatans offering a kind of genetic Elixir of Life.

As our knowledge of cell function increases, it is likely that genetic therapies will improve. One of the principle targets will be cancer cells, where the ultimate goal will be to get the cancerous cells to return in effect to their normal state. There is, however, another path to dealing with the problems of cells, and that is to create them to order, rather than trying to fix them up later. Genetic modification, which has already been introduced to a number of food crops and the production of the Harvard mouse, as well as drug producing bacteria, will come to humans. Some observers, such as Jeremy Rifkin, have already speculated on the potential smorgasbord of genetic choices that may be available to parents in the future. Everything from eye and hair colour, disease resistance, breast size, height, length of natural life, intelligence, and even musical ability may be modifiable. While the movies have tended to portray the genetic modification of people as an evil plot to create a super race (often in the form of relentless killing machine-soldiers), in reality the choice to modify human fetuses will be based largely on parental concern about providing the best life possible for their children. What will the world look like when the rich can modify themselves and the poor cannot?

CONCLUSION

As science has had a greater and greater role in shaping society, there has always been resistance to the changes it offers. At one level, it is wise to be cautious about the introduction of new products in a complex system. As the critic of technology Neil Postman has pointed out, the introduction of a new "thing," be it a device, practice, or ideology, changes society. It is not "society plus the computer," but a new society.[4] The conundrum of science in society is that the producers of science may not be the best people to judge what the impact of their products will be; however, because of the highly technical nature of the work, those who lack training may not understand the work well enough to make informed choices. Errors, flawed work, and other problems are inevitable, and the examples of DDT, thalidomide, and eugenics should stand as a warning that scientific mistakes can have dangerous consequences. The fact that there will be problems does not, however, mean that science should be rejected. Rather, it means that we must work to understand the potential benefits and problems of utilizing scientific developments.

Scientific research represents a complex interplay of social demands, technical constraints, and personal interests and abilities. It is not driven solely by ideas, but neither can it be produced to order. While science has provided some profound insights into the structure of nature, it has also presented us with some difficult questions about how to use that knowledge. Ironically, knowing more has made our choices more difficult rather than less. Understanding the history of science offers another venue for approaching these difficult questions, since it can show us the power and the danger of past choices and explain how we arrived at the world we live in. Science has, for example, been claimed as the basis for both Marxism and modern democracy.

The history of science can also be useful because it reveals the broader context of science rather than looking only at its products. No one owns science. If we wish to make informed choices, we must never forget that science exists because people created it, and it cannot exist separate from the community. Behind all the patents, prizes, and professional degrees, the idea of science—our long effort to understand nature—and the knowledge that radiates from that search, are part of our shared human heritage.

NOTES

1 1 nanometre = 1 millionth of a millimetre.

2 David Adam, "The Cheap Way to the Stars—by Escalator," *The Guardian* (13 September 2003): 6. See also, 2nd Annual Space Elevator Conference, 2003, available at www.isr.us/spaceelevatorconference.

3 Stuart H. Orkin, and Arno G. Motulsky, *Report and Recommendations of the Panel to Assess the NIH Investment in Research on Gene Therapy* (Bethesda, MD: NIH, 7 December 1995).

4 Neil Postman, *Technopoly* (New York, NY: Vintage, 1993).

Additional Credit Lines